THERAPIA VOLUME I

New insights into therapy and human behaviour

A selection of interviews from *The Therapist*

THERAPIA - VOLUME I

ISBN 1 899398 10 4

The Therapist Ltd.,
Henry House, 189 Heene Road, Worthing, West Sussex BN11 4NN

First published in *The Therapist,* journal of the European Therapy Studies Institute.

Printed in Great Britain by Redwood Books, Trowbridge, Wiltshire.

Contents

Introduction

THERAPIA contains a wonderfully rich collection of stories, experiences and reflections from a wide range of people on matters relating to understanding human behaviour and caring for others.

These thought provoking and challenging interviews first appeared in *The Therapist*, journal of the European Therapy Studies Institute (ETSI), a multi-disciplinary organisation concerned with gathering and publishing useful information and ideas on the subject from wherever they may be found.

They are reprinted here in book form because copies of many of them are out of print.

Note:

Think about what is missing from our culture.

Our collective cultural insanity

Doris Lessing *believes we are all much closer to craziness than we like to believe. In conversation with* ***Ivan Tyrrell*** *she talks about old age, breakdowns and the ubiquitous 'self-hater'.*

DORIS LESSING: I've been thinking a lot recently about an old woman I got to know, particularly with reference to the general awareness now about Alzheimer's, a word we spray around fairly lightly. I knew her for six or seven years before she finally died when she was over ninety.

She was, in fact, a pretty stupid woman of low intelligence. She had a poor childhood and married because it was expected of her. Most of her adult life she was a waitress and adored her work. She was a completely social person – she danced and had a wonderful pub life – and this social satisfaction was what she wanted from life.

At the age of sixty-five she was given the sack from her job because she was too old. Shortly after that her husband died. She had no pension and she went to pieces. From having the restaurant, where she worked and where everybody knew and loved her and she had a lot of friends, she became an old woman alone in her room. She became a drunk. People round here told me about it and, at the time I got to know her, she was into her eighties and totally demoralised. Although by then she was no longer drinking so much, she was in a filthy condition and could hardly get out of the flat. What really interested me about this was not the side issues about social services and so on, it was that, because she had never been anything else but a social person and couldn't cope with being alone, she got more and more stupid when she was on her own. Whenever you went to see her, if she had been alone for twenty-four hours, you'd think she was demented. I'm sure any doctor would say she was suffering from 'Alzheimer's' or senility or something, but I noticed if she had two or three people in to talk to her for a while, the craziness left her. She made sense. Sense on a pretty low level, but it *was* sense.

The point about her not being intelligent is relevant because, although she had always been a stupid woman, when she was normal, she made sense, was lively and quite funny. But whenever the services hadn't worked, and perhaps no one had seen her for two or three days, and I visited her, she was gone – totally barmy again!

This happened again and again. I would go and see her and, when I arrived, she would ramble and waffle. She didn't know what time of day it was, what day of the week, or the year. But, by the time I left, she would be making perfect sense again. She was properly herself.

Now this seems to me terribly important.

I cannot help but wonder how many old people are diagnosed as ill, or senile, when in fact they just need human contact.

IVAN TYRRELL: I'm sure that's true. I've also noticed that people who work on their own at home for long periods, for example, illustrators, behave oddly. I used to commission work from illustrators. Their work was detailed and time consuming requiring long periods of concentration. The artists often got obsessive about it and spent long, lonely hours working. And when I went to see them they would behave strangely for a while, either very extroverted – talking crazily *at* me for an hour or two, needing lots of attention – or be excessively introverted, taking ages to start talking and gradually becoming more themselves again. So people that work alone for days on end also get odd.

LESSING: But they weren't batty?

TYRRELL: Well, not disturbingly so. But illustrators and artists have a reputation for eccentricity and obsession and I think this is why. Some cultivate this, of course, but I noticed many times that, by spending time with them, they would get okay again. What you're saying is, if old people are left alone for days and weeks on end, they are bound to go crazy.

LESSING: And then they are given drugs by some busy doctor who says, 'This person is senile", or whatever. And then they get worse even more quickly.

There was a time when this old lady was told to take five different kinds of drugs each day. But no one ever asked what relation these drugs had to each other in her brain and body. She threw the drugs away when no one was looking, for which I applauded her. And then she became quite reasonable again.

But I wonder if people who look after the elderly are taught the concept that an old person living by themselves is not necessarily crazy but maybe just needs more contact with other people?

TYRRELL: They must be. Many people must have observed this.

LESSING: If it *is* taught they certainly didn't apply it to her. And, if it *isn't* taught, then that's pretty frightening.

TYRRELL: One nurse going round has to visit so many people. And these nurses are under so much pressure, they can only spare a few minutes with each one, which is sad if that visit is the highlight of that old person's week.

LESSING: At one time this particular old woman was getting visits most days from a nurse who would come in for five minutes to make sure she took her pills. A home help was also supposed to do an hour and a half a week with her but usually ended up doing ten minutes. A social worker would sweep in and out once a week for as short a time as possible. The person who helped her most was a good neighbour – she was the best of the lot.

What disturbed me was the readiness of the doctors to just drug her. I didn't see the point of that.

TYRRELL: That's how doctors are taught to treat people but many of them question this nowadays.

LESSING: It's a matter of luck what doctor you have.

I once met Dr. William Sargent who wrote *Battle for the Mind* and we were talking about drug treatments and he said, "Put yourself in my position. I'm sitting at my desk and in front of me is a totally depressed person and I know there's a good chance that this depression will be shifted by a course of a certain drug. Now, what would you do?" Well, I didn't know what to say because I should imagine one would try anything to get rid of depression. But what strikes me is that all these drug treatments are so hit and miss. No one really seems to know what they are doing. It's all, 'if it works, good. If not, let's try something else..."

TYRRELL: Do you know much about depression in other cultures?

LESSING: I only know that some cultures don't have a word for it. A doctor friend of mine who trained here in the west but is working out in Bangalore, told me that out there they bring in young women day after day who are totally depressed but it was no use talking to them in the language we use here – it was no good asking, "Are you unhappy?" or, 'Why are you unhappy?" or, "What do you think brought this on?" because happiness is not something that they feel they are entitled to. He had to develop a whole new approach to communicate with them. There was no way he could talk directly to the patient, he had to talk through the relatives, which was difficult because they were often responsible for the depression.

Peter Brent, who wrote among other things *Godmen of India*, mentioned in one of his books that a doctor in India would often take a mentally sick patient out of their family and into his own household to join his large, extended family. The idea was that a saner setting would cure the insane person. It's the opposite of putting people in mental hospitals. Apparently it often worked.

TYRRELL: There is a lot of evidence that depression and schizophrenia are due to people cracking up under impossible stresses from their family or work situation. The abnormal behaviours of schizophrenics often seem to be strategies for dealing with apparently irreconcilable situations.

LESSING: I think that we are all much nearer being crazy than we ever want to think about. I once sent myself crazy on purpose. I wrote about it in my book *The Four Gated City.* I had been struck by the fact that, if you read accounts of what shamans do when they initiate people, and what people experience in prison camps, and what schizophrenics and others describe, the symptoms are nearly always the same. They hear voices, become disassociated and have revelations. The thing they all have in common is that they haven't eaten or slept well.

Now this thought was precipitated by seeing what happened to a girl who was living in my house at the time. A tall, thin, beautiful girl who was unhappy in her love life. She didn't eat or sleep properly for weeks. One day she suddenly found herself floating above her own body looking down as she walked across Westminster Bridge.

So, okay, I thought, I'm going to try this - and I do not recommend this to anybody. I went down to my place in Devon where I knew I wouldn't be interrupted because it's difficult to have a couple of weeks by oneself in London. I went without food and sleep, deliberately watching everything that happened. It took about three days for me to begin going crazy. Then what happened was that a 'figure' appeared that I christened the 'self-hater'. It's a creature schizophrenics often describe. This figure, a person who shouts and screams at us, is obviously the conditioned conscience. It is what society creates in us, what daddy and mummy do to us; "Oh, you're a naughty girl", or, "Oh, you're a naughty boy." It exists inside one but sounds as if it's coming from outside.

Anyway, this voice yammering away in my head was terrifying because it was so strong. And two thoughts were running through my mind as this was happening. The first thought was that, if I wasn't moderately sophisticated in this area, I'd rush off and tell a doctor what I was experiencing and he would fill me full of drugs and probably have me sectioned. And the other thought was the fact that some of the hallucinations I was experiencing were common in all accounts of breakdowns. For example, 'the voyage', which appears in different cultures all over the world and takes different forms. If you're a Tibetan you have one type of journey or if you're Egyptian you have another. Christians have the stations of the cross. Ancient Greeks had Jason looking for the golden fleece. There is always a journey. And I had my journey.

So I watched all these things going on inside me which would have landed me in a loony bin if I didn't know what I was doing. Well, my time in Devon was coming to an end and, after two weeks, I started to eat and sleep properly again. It took a long time, at least three weeks, to get back to normal. So I think that perhaps a lot of people are having breakdowns, or described as schizophrenics, who are simply not eating or sleeping enough. Students studying for exams, for example, often go over the edge. People crossing the Atlantic in small boats hear God talking to them, especially when food is running low.

It also seems to me that it's people who have been brought up too rigidly in one way or another who have this 'self-hater' in them – this bullying, "you are naughty" figure. And it's not too far below the surface. So craziness is not quite as far away as we like to think.

TYRRELL: No, it's not. And, of course, sleep deprivation and poor diet have been used to manipulate people since time immemorial. But now this is well known it should be possible to help people who are suffering.

LESSING: That's right. It ought to be. Kurt Vonegutt's son had a schizophrenic breakdown in the 1960s. He went crazy and then wrote a stage by stage account of his breakdown and why it actually happened. He ended up giving the following advice to anyone subject to this kind of breakdown: eat three meals a day, take your vitamin pills, sleep properly, don't drink too much and never touch drugs, not even pot!

TYRRELL: That's interesting. Someone I know whose home

life was unhappy, recently began behaving oddly and is now under psychiatrists and labelled schizophrenic and, for several years, he hardly ate anything else other than bread and jam!

LESSING: Vitamins! For two or three years a doctor friend of mine in Sweden, a neurologist, has been testing the effects of diet and taking vitamins on two classes of people, schizophrenics and alcoholics. He discovered that poor diet and lack of vitamins create schizophrenics and alcoholics. And putting them on a proper diet cured a large percentage of them! The only thing was that he could never predict who was going to be cured. He couldn't be precise. All he could say was that, in this ward, X number will be cured if I give them plenty of vitamin B and a proper diet with all the vitamins they need.

TYRRELL: How else do you think we cope with craziness?

LESSING: Yesterday I visited a friend of mine who I knew first when I was twenty-one. He is tall, thin, bony, and was adopted when he was six months old. For the first six months of his life he was in an orphanage and it's clearly quite obvious that nobody cuddled him much. He's had several breakdowns but he's a painter and it's the painting that keeps him from going crazy. Nothing else helps. He can't drink because that drives him over the top. He needs his therapeutic, absorbing hobby to keep him relatively sane. People are that close to breakdown but they to find ways to cope. I know painting helps But it's not all that easy, is it? You can't just say to someone, "Why don't you take up painting because it's good for you?"

TYRRELL: No. When someone is suffering in depression it's hard for them to change direction themselves. Spike Milligan, who was labelled manic depressive, said that, when you are down, you don't take responsibility for your own psychological state. But the difficulty is that painting and similar therapeutic activities are something you do have to do *for yourself*, it has to come from within.

LESSING: That's the problem. You can't make people want to do something, even if it is what they need. Sometimes it helps to get people having a breakdown to talk about their feelings into a tape recorder. A doctor I knew, who treated angry, confused people, used to do that. He would say to them, "When you are alone and feel bad, talk into a tape recorder and tell me what you feel. It doesn't matter what you say, just say it. It doesn't matter if what you say makes sense or not. Shout it, scream it if necessary, but record what you are feeling for me to hear." And with some people that worked. It was like bursting a boil of pus.

TYRRELL: Some people just need someone to take a neutral interest when they're in a crisis and listen for a while in an accepting, supportive way.

LESSING: That's the trouble, isn't it? There aren't enough people to listen. I think that's why some find therapy successful because they are buying a friend, really. I had therapy when I was in my early 30s, for two or three years, a pretty relaxed affair. It wasn't analysis or anything like that. But now, when I look back, I know that I was buying a friend, someone who supported me all the time because I was being got at by so many people. It so happens she was a Jungian and a Roman Catholic, but she could have been anything. Anyway, people would say to me, "Isn't it just the same as having a very good friend listening to you?" But the patience of a good friend is limited. If they hear the same miseries day in and day out they get fed up.

TYRRELL: And time spent with a therapist is usually bound by a time limit, an hour or two a week. Also, a good therapist remains detached and knows how to promote a positive change, whereas a friend can get sucked in.

LESSING: Very easily! It doesn't take much. We can all go over the edge and disappear so quickly. A friend of mine was once very seriously depressed having an extremely bad time – and another person and I would take turns to go and listen to his depressing, monotone monologue. After a couple of hours I would find myself thinking, "That's right, what is the point to it all? You might just as well die. You haven't got the life you want. You haven't got any friends... and I had to rush off before I was overwhelmed and lost my sanity. It's difficult not to get sucked in. Depression seems to me to be the worst of all, much worse than schizophrenia.

TYRRELL: There's a hell of a lot of it about

LESSING: I wonder why? I know several people who get deeply depressed and they say it is the most painful thing *physically*. I couldn't understand this until three years ago when I really experienced the emotion of grief for the first time. It was not depression, but grief and anguish. It is an emotion that expresses itself physically.

TYRRELL: Heartache! The heart is supposed to be only a pump yet there is a tremendous tightness and pain around the heart that's associated with these strong emotions.

LESSING: Jung said somewhere in one of his books that he would very often have a patient sitting in front of him who is completely in a trap in their life situation and neither he nor his patient could see any possible way out. Then he would meet this person four or five days later and find their problem had been solved in a way that neither of them could possibly have foreseen. And then he said something like this, that you have to have faith in the unconscious guide in the unconscious part of the person you are trying to help.

I'm sure that's true because you do see people who seem as if they are shut in a dark room and yet, somehow or other they get out, or somebody unexpectedly helps them out.

Another thing I have found is that you should never give up on anybody. That I'm quite sure of because, over and over again, and I'm sure you've had the same experience, we see people who are an absolute dead loss. Hopeless cases. And yet they can, quite unexpectedly, be transformed later in their life. So, never give up on anyone, hard as it may seem sometimes.

One of the best ways to overcome that miserable feeling

in the morning when you think, 'Oh my God, I really can't face it!' is to smile! You don't want to smile. You don't feel like smiling. But if you move the set of your facial muscles into a smile it cheats your brain and changes the chemical balances in such a way that you quickly feel much better. I find it works like anything!

TYRRELL: Yes, that's partly why laughter is so therapeutic.

LESSING: I have a rather fanciful interpretation about schizophrenia, which is probably nonsense, but it might interest some people. It is that this self-hater part of ourselves, the conditioned conscience, is usually disassociated and is just sitting there ready to pounce. Then, when some crisis activates it, it gets plugged into the entire human psyche. It isn't just personal, it becomes an impersonal accuser, as if the whole of society is behind it. And that's why people can't bear it. It's so powerful. It isn't just the voice of daddy or mummy, it's the total collective power of dislike, accusation and pure hatred. In other cultures this is probably a recognised aspect of a god – I wouldn't be surprised – certainly in India you'd find it, probably Kali or another of those terrible goddesses. But I'm sure that schizophrenics get plugged into something so enormously powerful they can't bear it.

TYRRELL: Perhaps that's why schizophrenics commonly believe they are being spied on by evil alien creatures.

LESSING: They often think they're spied on through electric light bulbs or electric sockets on skirting boards.

The latest one I've heard about is the check-out points at supermarkets! There is an interesting cult in South Africa which I was told about. They believe that the world is being controlled by an evil force, '666', which is taking over the entire world through the agency of check-outs in supermarkets. And this is easily proved because so often the numbers on the printouts from these check-outs have 666 on them. You can't fault the logic of crazy people! And this cult now has a paid up membership. They are waiting

for Satan. South Africa breeds amazing cults for some reason.
TYRRELL: Cults in human groups seem to form as automatically as crystals.
LESSING: Yes, they do. One of my most amazing and improbable memories is from New York in the 70s. I was walking across Central Park when I saw a man in a dressing gown, sitting cross-legged on the grass, surrounded by people. And I asked my friend, "Who is that chap?" She said, "That man started coming into Central Park lunchtimes for a break as regular as clockwork and he always sat down on the grass in some kind of robe. Before long people gathered and sat around him. He became known as the silent guru. Every day people appeared and sat with him through the lunch-hour for his 'silent benediction'. He never opened his mouth. He never said a word. Then summer ended, and no one sat on the grass any more. Apparently the man himself was immensely tickled by the whole thing.

That's how easy it is to create a legend and a cult.
TYRRELL: That reminds me of the Middle Eastern story of the traveller whose favourite donkey died on a pilgrimage. He was heartbroken when he buried the donkey and wept over its grave and people came by and saw how distraught he was. He was too upset to speak and the people assumed a holy man had died and built a tomb over the donkey's grave. People started to visit the tomb to receive blessings from the 'saint' they believed it contained. Eventually a town grew up around the tomb.
LESSING: That's a lovely story. It's supposed to be true.
TYRRELL: I know you feel that our culture, and the way we live and entertain ourselves, blunts our sensibilities and prevents us absorbing more subtle ideas and feelings. Can you expand on this?
LESSING: Well, we are all sensation junkies, aren't we? Everything has to be bigger and better and louder and more noteworthy. I've been wondering about music a lot recently – I'm sure I'm not the first to wonder about it – and this is

related to this problem. In past cultures it was always believed that music had powerful effects on our state of mind and people acted accordingly. War dance music, for example, was used to send men off to fight. Soldiers still march to music to bind them together. Patriotic music is used for every kind of occasion to whip up strong feelings of national identity. Shamans used music to induce trance states. All religions use music to generate emotions that they, I think mistakenly, believe are 'spiritual'. And we are told by genuine spiritual teachers that music is very powerful and has been used, under precise, controlled, conditions to assist with human development. And yet we now deluge ourselves in music day and night, usually extremely loudly, as if the effects were of no consequence. I wonder if we will ever ask ourselves what this is doing to us?

You know what it's like when something strikes you and you can't understand why you never saw it before? Well, it's like this for me with this musical deluge. I ask myself, how is it possible that we don't question it? We switch on the radio and listen to music, we switch it off and think, well, I wouldn't mind listening to a tape, and we listen to that. Some people even go round with music channelled straight into their ears and brain. But what is it doing to us?

Supposing continuous loud sounds are partly responsible for crime. It's a big jump, I know, but kids are not only saturated with television culture, which I'm sure is harmful, they're blasted with an excess of music. What sort of imbalance does that create in people and has anyone researched this?

TYRRELL: Well, there was the research done in Canada on the effects of music. They had two groups of people. One attended a concert of exquisite, spiritual, uplifting music, and the other group heard no music in the previous twenty four hours. Both groups were then shown graphic details of a disgusting and violent crime and were asked to assess the sort of punishment that should be given to the perpetrator.

The unexpected result was that the people who had just left the 'spiritually uplifting' concert reacted in far more judgmental, cruel and insensitive way than those who just pottered through the day without hearing any music. The people who had heard the music tended to say the criminal should be executed, castrated or whatever. And the other group were more rational and would say things like, "He's a very sick man", "He needs treatment", and so on.

The thing that struck me about this is that all music raises the emotional temperature – and emotional temperature doesn't discriminate. I think we're not, as we like to believe, 'spiritually uplifted' by Mozart, but we are emotionally aroused. And this is a different thing entirely.

Music is designed to manipulate our emotions. Film makers are experts at this. All films are an exercise in manipulating emotions with music, which is often highly enjoyable, but perhaps we should be more aware of it.

LESSING: More research is needed I think. My generation were swamped in highly emotional, usually yearning, loving music – mostly from the 20s and 30s. We listened to it day and night and I wonder if we were not enormously sentimentalised by it. Nowadays the music is more pounding – often with an air of brutal violence about it. This must reach a completely different area of our minds.

TYRRELL: I'm sure it does.

LESSING: Ever since I can remember things have got louder and more dramatic. It is almost as if we can't hear anything that isn't put dramatically. And we don't ask ourselves what it is doing to us. You can't see a television programme without music. They can't show a deer running across a mountainside without a sentimental tune of some kind.

TYRRELL: Even news programmes start with music!

LESSING: It's taken for granted that music is a good thing. It's incredible to me that this should be such an unexamined area.

TYRRELL: Well, the people that examine it in one kind of

way are those who make and use music – composers, performers, film makers, programme makers, advertisers etc. They use it to influence us so, in a sense, they have researched it because they know what works.
LESSING: But it isn't the sort of research that I would regard as useful. And this is because most people automatically think that music is a good thing. We should challenge our assumptions. Is music good for us? Is even classical music good and ennobling?
TYRRELL: The research that *has* been done seems to show it isn't. But few people would like that idea.
LESSING: I don't think we've begun to ask the range of questions about how we are manipulated and why we allow ourselves to be. Newspapers are another area which I think needs looking at. We disturb ourselves by buying newspapers. When I see a compartment in a train full of people reading just two or three different newspapers, it looks to me like mass brainwashing which we willingly allow. I crave print if I'm deprived of it. I'm a print junkie.
TYRRELL: It's addictive...
LESSING: There are other things about ourselves we don't notice because they're taken so much for granted. Politics, for a start, which seems to become more and more like theatre and less to do with real information. Politics has become an entertainment similar to gambling. Look at our ridiculous election days for example, where we sit up all night watching all the prediction apparatus, trying to find out who will win, a fact we will all know anyway at 8 o'clock the following morning. The nation is locked into a gambling mentality.
TYRRELL: I think it's all part of raising the emotional temperature, using anything that is happening for emotional excitement which we mistake for 'being more real'. But then we are being manipulated.
LESSING: True. The common denominator is the emotional temperature.

Idries Shah, who introduced many new ideas into the

spiritual and psychological tradition of Sufism said to me a long time ago that he had observed that our Western culture is soaked in two assumptions – we believe that politics and sex are the solution to everything. We never examine this so we don't know the extent by which we're manipulated by these assumptions. The corollary is that we find it extremely hard to look at previous cultures because they didn't have these assumptions. Past cultures operated by completely different sets of expectations and demands than those that operate us.

Now I believe we have to add to two other stimulants, crime and killing, to these assumptions. These are a major voyeuristic feature of television every night. They are now doing real life reconstructions, horrific crimes lovingly recreated, two or three times a week. Even serious newspapers regularly include 'real life crime' stories in grizzly detail because they know it sells papers.

TYRRELL: Shah also said that, when he was younger, he had expected Westerners to take on board with enthusiasm all the information that modern research was revealing about human behaviour. He thought that this would be necessary as a precursor to further human development and had hoped it would happen much as the world absorbed the necessity for hygiene in the 19th century. But, over the years, he found it wasn't being absorbed, except in highly selective ways which unbalances us. He thought that the main reason for this was that the truth about ourselves is not emotionally exciting enough.

LESSING: I know, I find this when I'm interviewed. An interview is usually a map of the mind of the interviewer. I can go through a whole interview replying to questions that totally bore me.

The interviewers usually say, "What would you like to talk about?" And I say, "Well, this is what really interests me..." and I might like to talk, for example, about the discoveries of Edward T. Hall which he wrote up in books like *The Silent*

Language and *The Dance of Life.* His books are full of revolutionary observations about what we are like – he explored the unspoken ideas behind cultures and the rhythms of time and life – but he is hardly known. But the interviewers' faces fall and they quickly steer me back to my childhood, feminism or how many words a minute I write.

TYRRELL: Have you ever tried to talk to interviewers about human behaviour?

LESSING: Yes. They are not interested.

TYRRELL: And they don't publish it?

LESSING: Not only that, I can see they literally don't hear what I am saying.

TYRRELL: Have any of them asked you in any depth about your interest in what Sufis have observed and know about culture and human behaviour?

LESSING: Not really. The nearest some of them get is to say, "Oh, I hear you are a Sufi.' And by that you know immediately that they are quite ignorant of the subject. They, if they have thought about it at all, probably think Sufism is a cult – an easy mistake to make because there are many cults that call themselves Sufis. So then I stop them and what I say now is, "I've been studying this for a long time. It's what interests me more than anything else, but I don't want to make a series of cliché remarks which will then be misunderstood by you and your readers." And then I tell them that people who are really interested will find the necessary books that are freely available. That does the trick – they usually have amnesia about even having asked the question!

But sometimes I meet people as I travel around who are more serious and have studied the material and it has struck a chord in them. In Singapore recently I met two ordinary young men who wanted to talk about Shah's work. I can meet such people anywhere and can talk seriously about it. But interviewers are generally not interested in ideas and knowledge, not really.

The observations and evidence that Shah has presented

about the way the world really works I continually find astonishing. Many of his ideas are now common currency. Thirty years ago they were unknown and, unless you can remember the shock of hearing these ideas when they were new to us, you cannot credit it because we think we've always thought like we do now. I see them around all over the place now. For example, he was the first to draw attention to all the different levels of importance of giving and receiving attention, and distinguishing the difference between *wants* and *needs* – which seems familiar and obvious now, but was quite startling and new in the 60s.

And the idea that most of what we do is fuelled by greed, even acts that appear altruistic, is now quite common but it wasn't at all then. When a new idea starts floating around I often think that it is something we first heard from Shah not so long ago, or it's in one of his books. I think the way he deliberately put ideas into our culture is an astonishing cultural phenomena.

TYRRELL: It's a sort of seeding, isn't it?

LESSING: Yes it is. There are things that we need to know about ourselves that might take generations to take root, but the ideas have to be planted. It's certainly happening. But few people notice, or are interested in, long term changes to whole cultures, changes that take generations to occur.

TYRRELL: But certain types of people are attracted to the larger view. It's one of the reasons the best of science fiction is so stimulating.

LESSING: Yes. And the rises and falls of civilisations provide a quite distinct excitement from the 'little girl having an emergency operation' type of story that we have evolved to get excited about. An observation I think about often is to the effect that, once we played with toys but now our toys play with us'. It's true! From cars to weapons! TV to computers. Everything! Our lives are determined by our inventions, which is why the Frankenstein theme is so popular.

Another thing that interests me is the fact that we have binary minds. We always have to have an 'either/or' I see myself and others affected by this all the time. For example, if I'm giving a lecture, invariably half the questions begin, "Mrs Lessing, do you think this or do you think that?" "Is it A or B?" and I say, "Well, it's both, or something else entirely", this satisfies nobody.

But this is how we think. We take some element out of a subject or a person and use that to label it or them for ever after. It's as if we can only have one idea or fact – so we have to choose. We can't have a pattern in our minds about the subject or person, we have to have a single label that we can refer to all the time.

TYRRELL: It is unusual to find people who can look at a person and see them as a pattern. We're tremendously influenced by first impressions. When we meet somebody for the first time, if they happen to be angry or sad or laughing or frivolous, that is the impression that colours our lifelong image of that person. Later, when we know them much better, we still judge their actions against that first impression.

Instead of actually looking at someone and thinking, "This is a person who at this moment is laughing," and knowing, as we all must know intellectually, that the person must have a vast hinterland of other behavioural reactions in different circumstances, we still work on this ridiculous labelling assumption.

LESSING: And we can't make much progress while we simplify everything like this. But I wonder why we do it?

TYRRELL: It's left brain functioning. I suppose it had and still has its uses. I mean, you can get on if you remove doubt by labelling things, even if the label doesn't bear scrutiny. The trouble is, most of the time we are not aware we are doing it.

LESSING: It's easier to see it going on in another culture. In China it is so obvious. I went there recently and they have a slogan for absolutely everything. They never seem to analyse a problem, they reduce it to a label. "Let a thousand flowers bloom..." or something.

I spoke to a Chinese official there, one of a whole group of young directors and writers, and I said that, from the outside, China struck us as a culture that swung very easily from one extreme to the other...

TYRRELL: ... like a vast shoal of fish, all moving as one...

LESSING: ... yes. Immediately the Chinese in the group started laughing at me because they knew that I meant that, at the moment, they were in a liberal swing. And they told me the story of a friend of theirs who had written a novel about the awful state of morale in China's army where the soldiers have just about as bad a time as Russian soldiers. This novel exposed the situation – he was allowed to write it because openness is supposed to reign now. But it was sent back from the censor with the following remark – 'Not every writer can be published. Not every book can be printed.' And that was the end of that. Everybody accepted it! That's what they are like. They have got labelling down to a fine art.

TYRRELL: That's worrying. The Chinese are going to have so much power over us soon.

LESSING: They don't give a damn about Europe and the things we think important. They have a saying which I find rather endearing. Every time they are criticised about ill-treating people or whatever, they will say, "Ah yes, the Yangtze always flows East, as they say." And that's the end of the matter.

My father used to say that people like me have no idea at all what the minds of people were like when he was a child. He was brought up in the country near Colchester and said that people then didn't think about the world much at all. And if they thought about something happening in Europe, it was quite rare. What they thought about was the local scene – who is going to win the next race in the school picnic etc. And going up to London was a great treat. This provincialism was what a person's mind was like. And that must have been true for the whole of Europe, unless you were very rich. Then the First World War changed everything. Suddenly the outside world exploded into everyone's consciousness and there were films, radio, and so on. He said that, between his mind and his father's mind, there was a total gulf and between his mind and my mind was a total gulf. His father would not have believed that anyone could go to the moon. He would have just laughed at the idea – and at television and so on – all facts that we now take for granted. Now we think we know everything that happens everywhere in the world. But this deceives us because we have no idea what's important. There is nothing in us that really knows how to select those bits of information that are valuable. It's all on a par. Sadly, the way we entertain new ideas seems to depend almost entirely on whether they're exciting or not. Hardly anybody is interested in real information.

TYRRELL: People do get interested in little exciting bits, especially if they can be marketed, like NLP or 'How to Use Both Sides of Your Brain', just little pieces of information really, but people build careers on them.

LESSING: Edward de Bono did that.

TYRRELL: Many people do it. Exploiting information instead of absorbing it is one of *my* difficulties!

LESSING: For years my problem has been that I am much too emotional about everything and this over-emotional response is a great enemy. As you say, emotion stops us seeing what's really going on. But I don't know, you see, how much like other people I am. Am I worse or just the same? Is everyone so emotionally oriented? I don't know.

An interesting thing happened when I gave a lecture to the Institute of Cultural Research on 'Barriers to Perception'. I listed ten barriers to perception, one of which was guilt. Now, come question time, nobody asked a question about anything but guilt! People still stop me now and say, "remember that lecture you gave about guilt?" This is astonishing to me! What are we so guilty about? Why are we all so ridden with guilt. What is this about? Maybe it's this embodied accuser again.

TYRRELL: I wonder if it's because we are not doing something which some part of us, deep within, knows we should be doing?

LESSING: Well, I think that's possibly true. With these emotions I've got myself now to the point where I am able to watch them proliferating away and can detach from them. But it isn't easy. Shah once said that, if you are in a state of terrific emotion, it's possible and useful to switch into another mode by, for example, doing an arithmetical problem in your head, or something else very unemotional like listening to arousing music, then switching it off and doing a crossword puzzle – you use a completely different part of your brain.

TYRRELL: To do that on command would be wonderful, wouldn't it?

LESSING: Yes. But I find it almost impossible although I am better at it now. The interesting thing is that I wrote that tip down and forgot all about it until I re-read my diary last month. I had completely forgotten!

TYRRELL: Well, that's probably because the emotional part of your mind doesn't want you to think about it. It feels threatened and is protecting itself

LESSING: Do you think everybody lives their lives in a tumult of emotion in one form or another? Because, if so, it's a pretty horrific thought. Even the so called intellect is emotional. In fact, in my experience, intellectuals are *very* emotional.

TYRRELL: A lot of intellectual activity seems to me to be a strategy for suppressing or dealing with emotions, and the emotions often cause intellectuals to behave in peculiar ways, which is why they so often appear, despite their 'cleverness', to be blind to the obvious. It's an unthinking strategy. Although it's intellectual, it's done automatically. We can't help doing it.

LESSING: Yes. The sad thing is, all these issues about human behaviour are so important, and so fundamental to why people get ill, anxious, sad and behave criminally, that they ought to be looked at calmly and scientifically by more people and talked about more widely. But these issues are not explored much on TV or in other media and yet they are far more important than politics or the 'arts'. That's why what you're doing with *The Therapist* is so valuable.

Treating depression

Dr Michael Yapko, one *of America's leading research workers on new, brief therapy treatments for depression, talks to* ***Ivan Tyrrell*** *about how they are helping sufferers.*

IVAN TYRRELL: I find it refreshing that in your books, lectures and workshops, you go out of your way to stress the importance of using research findings to dispel myths about human behaviour.
MICHAEL YAPKO: That's right. Research and effectiveness are the only things that hold up.
TYRRELL: What has research revealed to give hope to depressed people?
YAPKO: It shows us therapists that there are certain things to do and certain things not to do. Medication alone, for example, is still a common choice of treatment for depression used by many psychotherapists. But we now know they should reconsider what they are doing.
TYRRELL: Why?
YAPKO: When you look at the epidemiological studies, as well as the cross-cultural studies, they show clearly that depression is a learnt phenomenon, not a biological illness. Despite the popularity of the disease model, it's not entirely appropriate to depression. The rate of relapse when using medication, for example, is much higher than when using cognitive therapy.

There are still cultures on this planet where depression is a non-existent phenomena.
TYRRELL: Such as?
YAPKO: One is the Kaluli tribe in New Guinea. That's a culture where, as far as psychiatric anthropologists can tell, depression is non-existent. Also, amongst the Amish people, depression is a fraction of what it is in the rest of American society. It's no coincidence that both those societies are structured in an entirely different way from the majority of

Western cultures today. They place a huge premium on community, on being connected, on immediate resolution of problems, on leaving no lingering niggles that, five years later, are still being dragged through the courts. They do all the things we don't any more, which is why, when you look at cross-cultural studies, you always see that, as any society Westernises itself, its rates of depression go correspondingly up. The trend is clear. Clinical depression now influences the course of literally millions of peoples' lives. All research surveys confirm what most of us in the mental health profession intuitively know - that depression is a large and growing problem.

TYRRELL: What do you think causes this trend?

YAPKO: There is something very toxic about the way we construct our society. We have an over-crowded world where people are dying of loneliness! We place the emphasis on *me*, and what *I* think and what *I* feel. And there is no real emphasis on connection any more.

The demographic age breakdowns of who gets depressed are fairly startling. The so called baby-boomers, those born since 1945, have a rate of depression nearly ten times higher than that of their grandparents. This suggests that biology plays a considerably lesser role in depression than sociology and psychology. And that is also borne out in terms of treatment results because, when someone is given psychiatric medication and antidepressants exclusively, they have a far higher rate of relapse than somebody who goes through appropriate psychotherapy.

The psychotherapy of choice today is cognitive therapy which employs the mind's ability to change its mental structure and content. And, riding very closely behind, is interpersonal therapy. These are the two approaches that have demonstrated themselves to be the best treatments for depression. Most depression experts will tell you that the ideal is a combination of the two.

Antidepressant medication should be used for short term

symptom relief only. Cognitive therapy and personal therapy are essential for prevention of symptom relapse.
TYRRELL: The Peter Breggin book *Toxic Psychiatry* attacks the way the medical/pharmaceutical establishment still promotes drugs to treat depression and other 'mental illnesses'. Did that book cause much of a stir in the States?
YAPKO: I don't think it did because all the people making progress in the field don't rely exclusively on drugs anyway. Mainstream psychiatry got diluted fifteen years ago. Lawsuits do that to a field.
TYRRELL: Oh, that's why we are slower to change over here, is it? We're not such a litigious society!
YAPKO: Do you know what Crackerjack is? Do you have it in England?
TYRRELL: I don't think so.
YAPKO: It's a caramel-coated popcorn with peanuts that comes in a box. In every box there is supposed to be a little toy surprise. A couple sued Crackerjack when their child opened up a box and there wasn't a toy surprise inside!
TYRRELL: Emotional damage, eh?
YAPKO: Yes. Emotional distress... It's crazy! A man went to a drive-in McDonald's where you stay in your car, wind down your window, get your order and drive off. He bought a milk-shake and drove off. As he went along he started drinking it and split some on himself and caused a traffic accident. He then sued McDonald's because he said they should have printed a warning on the cup saying, 'Don't Drink and Drive'.
TYRRELL: I'm not a fan of McDonald's but I hope he lost. The mere idea that some legal adviser could say, "Yes, you've got a case there", is astonishing. Legal systems like that just sap a country of all strength.
YAPKO: Yes. But this fear of litigation makes psychiatrists and therapists more careful about the effectiveness of what they do. Therapists, for example, that implant ideas in people about them being sexually abused in childhood and repressing it, are under attack through the courts now - and

rightly so. In the same way, psychiatrists who use brain damaging amounts of neuroleptics, anti-psychotics, stimulants, antidepressants or tranquillising drugs have been restrained by the fear of legal proceedings.

TYRRELL: That's good to hear.

YAPKO: When I first began studying depression, nearly twenty years ago now, very little was known. It was considered a sub-category of manic depressive illness and the widely held assumption was that it was biologically caused. Likewise, unfortunately, very little was known in terms of what to do about it. If someone even had the presence of mind to know that he or she were depressed and attempted to seek professional help, there was a very good chance that all the therapist could or would do with their time would be to say, in essence, "Cheer up!".

Trite suggestions were given like, "Pull yourself up by your boot-straps", "Behind every cloud there is a silver lining", "It's always darkest before the dawn", and countless other clichés that were meant to help but could offer little realistic means for doing so. Depressed people were even made to feel guilty if they were depressed. People would say to them, "What have you got to be depressed about? Go and work in a hospital and see what real suffering is like!"

Being depressed is bad enough, but to make the person feel guilty for it, as if they were malingering or to blame in some way, is a massive additional burden to put on them.

Nowadays, depression is probably one of the best understood of all the lesser psychological disorders. When it is the primary diagnosis, and there is no diagnosis of a personality disorder with it, it is highly responsive to good treatment, generally within twelve sessions.

Getting the symptom remissions is not the difficult part. That you can do with the medication alone. The difficult part is preventing relapses and teaching the person how to re-interpret life experiences in a way that isn't depressing. Depression is basically a viewpoint of life. For most people it is not a disease. It is not usually something rooted in faulty biology - meaning faulty genetics or biochemistry. Rather depression is usually a product of one's outlook and one's way of responding to life experience.

In this respect, what matters most is how the combination of an individual's personal history, and the socialisation derived from the culture they live in, comes together to form his or her life perspective.

TYRRELL: Please expand on that.

YAPKO: By life perspective I mean one's way of both interpreting and responding to various life experiences. This is not to say that biology plays no role in depression, because it is obvious that biology plays a significant role in all aspects of our experience. In fact, it could even be said that we are biologically predisposed to be sensitive to our environment and culture. But research indicates quite clearly that depression is, for most people, a product of *learning*.

From the therapeutic standpoint that is most encouraging because what can be learned can be unlearned and what was never learned can be taught.

TYRRELL: Why are some people more prone to depression than others?

YAPKO: I believe it is because life is an ambiguous stimulus. Life is so amorphous it becomes whatever we make it out to be. Life does not have any inherent meaning, it simply offers us opportunities to project on to it whatever matters to each of us, based on our own unique backgrounds and make-up. Some projections make us feel great. "Life is meant to be enjoyed to the fullest, using each precious moment to revel in the beauty of the world." Some projections make us feel terrible. "Life is a bitch, and then you die!" It's negative views like this that have a great deal to do with clinical depression - a disorder featuring an intricate system of negative projections about self, life, the universe, most everything.

If I call you up at two in the afternoon and you're not home, and I leave a message on your answering machine.

"Hi there Ivan, it's Michael. Call me back", and it's now eight o'clock at night, and you haven't called me back. If I'm depressed, I'll say either, "He must be mad at me", or, "He's avoiding me. He doesn't like me. Why do I always alienate people? What's wrong with me? Why can't I have friends like other people? Why do people abandon me? There must be something really wrong with me." And I feel progressively worse and worse. I could end up intensely suicidal because you didn't return my message.

If I'm not depressed, however, and you didn't call me back, my explanation is far more likely to be. "Ivan's busy, maybe he hasn't got the message yet or maybe his answering machine is broken."

And so it's useful to look at depression as a product of what's called 'attributional style' - a person's characteristic way of explaining why he hurts.

This is especially true of trauma. When something bad happens in a person's life we can find out whether they blame themselves for it, or whether they believe it's a permanent or temporary thing - if they believe it affects their entire life or is just limited to that particular segment of it.

So the relationship between attributional style and the experience of depression as well as how someone's going to react to treatment is very important. And a lot of what good therapy is about is basically teaching people to change their attributional styles.

TYRRELL: Is that the single most important finding from research into the treatment of depression?

YAPKO: I think so. We know that there is no one single cause for depression and no single solution. Coming to the realisation that depression is a product of outlook and learned patterns for handling life experience, gives us a new focus in therapy. We can dismiss out of hand the notion that depression is a sign of character weakness or mental instability. Likewise, we can reject summarily the kind of perspectives that end up blaming the victim by suggesting that somehow the individual *likes* to be depressed, or gets rewarded in some way for being depressed.

With this new focus has also come the realisation that we don't have to spend inordinate amounts of time exploring the past and, in fact, have developed approaches that can very reliably treat depression on a short-term basis. The majority of depressed individuals will respond well to these methods in a range of only one to twelve sessions.

Brief therapy methods have some specific characteristics. The emphasis in these methods is on specific, concretely defined patterns, not vague and abstract issues. Brief therapy methods place little emphasis on what I've come to call psychological archeology. In other words, *why* someone gets depressed is considered less important than *how* depression develops. We look at how a person thinks, how they respond, how they gather and organise information, how they decide on a particular course of action, and how they establish contact with, or ignore, different parts of themselves in different situations. This approach provides us with the focal point of treatment.

When I speak of depression as a by-product of either ineffective or inappropriate lifestyle patterns, it means that the person's ability to respond meaningfully and skilfully to a given situation is somehow impaired.

TYRRELL: How does it become impaired?

YAPKO: By focusing on irrelevant or even hurtful aspects of experience and by amplifying certain thoughts or feelings and situations where they would be better de-emphasised. Or by misinterpreting experience and generating irrelevant or hurtful responses to those misinterpretations.

That's why brief therapy methods emphasise *how* a person does something rather than *why*.

The guiding principle is a simple one. If what you are doing isn't working - isn't getting you the results that you want - then it's not only advisable, but it's necessary to do something different.

Consistent with that idea is that the therapeutic method used should emphasise thinking differently, responding differently, interpreting and doing things differently.

Therapy is very much a collaborative process of cooperation between a therapist and a client which emphasises learning - learning to think differently and respond differently. The emphasis on a collaborative relationship between the therapist and client cannot be overstated. It is the therapist's role to provide direction to help the client clearly define goals and identify the steps that it's necessary to take in order to achieve them. The therapist creates the learning opportunities that will foster the development of the skills necessary to succeed. It is the client's participation, however, by becoming active in his or her own growth process, that catalyses the therapy and makes good things happen.

The emphasis throughout every therapy session I conduct with depressed individuals, is on *action* - not analysis, and not the endless hashing and rehashing of unchangeable, historical facts. The emphasis is on *action* and not rumination, for a number of reasons, but in particular to counter the typically passive demeanour of the depressive, who often feels helpless and has only negative expectations. It is vital to the therapy process to engage the client in the action of doing things differently.

TYRRELL: So, what then makes a good therapist from the point of view of treating depression?

YAPKO: A good therapist with a depressed client is not going to focus on the past - not going to rake up every past hurt, every past disappointment, every past rejection, every past humiliation. The source of the person's attributional style is irrelevant. The focus has to be on teaching the person ways to change their outlook *now* on the way things are going to happen tomorrow.

A good therapist will mobilise the depressed person for the future. The therapy will be active rather than insight-oriented. It will concentrate on change. Rather than focusing on the past, it will focus on the future.

A good therapist will not surround and cuddle a depressed person - hold them and say, "There, there."

A good therapist will say, "Get moving!"

A good therapist is constantly challenging the depressed person - in a supportive way - but constantly challenging nonetheless. They get the client to question their viewpoints and experience of life.

TYRRELL: In practical terms what would you actually say?

YAPKO: I might say something like, for example, "Gee that's an interesting interpretation about why she said 'no' to you for asking her out. But can you think of any other reasons that she might have for turning you down?" A depressed person will always jump to conclusions that say, "I'm a reject, I'm no good and that's why she said no." It would never occur to him that she's married, or has other commitments or that maybe she's a lesbian. He has just never thought about it. He would automatically jump to a negative, hurtful conclusion and accept it as true.

That's one of the most basic strategies for treating depression; to get the client to challenge their own explanations. When an event happens to depress a person, as it always will, I encourage them to generate at least five different plausible explanations for why the event might have happened. And then I get them to find evidence to support each one. They then start to realise that there are at least five different ways of looking at it, and then they have to question why they always choose the one that hurts them.

TYRRELL: Where does your use of hypnosis come in?

YAPKO: Knowing that our views on life are arbitrary, and therefore malleable, makes using hypnosis the most effective way forward. This is because it's the field that has a better than average grasp of the complex notion that reality is essentially a subjectively created and experienced phenomena. I believe I have broken new ground by formally bringing together depression as a problem, and hypnosis as a solution. It is a pairing of problem and treatment that is long overdue.

The best and most powerful learning comes from your own direct experience. And the important lessons that last a lifetime are the ones that touch you in the deepest places within you and leave a very powerful association in that place. My emphasis on experiential learning is consistent with my emphasis on the use of hypnosis.

Clinical hypnosis is a process of experiential learning and its general purpose is to build a meaningful and effective frame of mind. As I suggested, depression is a frame of mind. It's a way of looking at, and responding to, life experiences. So hypnosis is a powerful means for building a frame of mind that interprets and generates responses to life that work more effectively.

Many psychiatrists, using outdated concepts of depression and treatment, used to prevent recovery from depression by focusing people on their relationship with their mother and father, their childhood and so on, encouraging endless analysis of every unchangeable, historical fact.

We now know that, not only is that unnecessary for therapy to progress, it actually delays therapy progressing by side-tracking the person into irrelevancies.

Just as there were old out-dated concepts of depression which prevented or delayed the development of brief therapy approaches, there were old, out-dated concepts of hypnosis which likewise prevented its beneficial use in the treatment process. But, just as we have come to learn a lot about the nature of depression, we have come to learn a lot about the nature of hypnosis. The old misconceptions have fallen by the wayside and now we are quite clear that hypnosis is a valuable ally in communicating ideas and helping someone to organise and form a different way of interpreting and responding to life experiences.

Hypnosis is not a therapy. Hypnosis does not provide a

cure, rather hypnosis is a way of doing therapy and is perhaps best thought of as a way of communicating important messages in an absorbing way. In that respect, what is therapeutic about hypnosis is its ability to stimulate new ideas and perspectives. Hypnosis is not the therapeutic agent, rather it is the new associations established in the client's mind *during* the hypnosis that facilitate the real therapeutic gain. Hypnosis can be used to encourage the client to develop new resources or to apply familiar ideas in new ways and in new situations.

I use hypnosis to facilitate flexibility in the person's thinking and to build positive expectations towards the future. I do a lot of age progression work. I also use hypnosis to reduce their agitation and anxiety.

One of the chief characteristics of the depressive is the tendency to ruminate, to spin around in their mind, over and over again, all their depressing thoughts, and so I use hypnosis to curtail the ruminations. There are many ways of using hypnosis and I've detailed them in my books on the subject. They are all hypnotic strategies for building frames of mind in the therapy session. And then, by using task assignments with the person outside in the real world, challenging their own perceptions about things. I'm constantly setting up behavioural experiments and circumstances that force the person to challenge their own world viewpoint.

TYRRELL: You've got to take great care with such interventions, have you not? It's a serious responsibility.

YAPKO: Well, I do take it seriously. The fact that somebody's in a position of being a therapist means that, by virtue of title alone, they are wielding considerable power.

There are various different ways of looking at power; from the ability to reward to the ability to punish, to the ability to make identifications. And one form of power is what's known as 'expert power'. This is the fact that a client views you as knowing more than they do - because if they knew anything about it, they would have already solved their problem. They see you as the trained expert. So if you then say to them, "What you need to do is to catch some flies and make them into a sandwich and eat it", you will get a significant percentage of people who will go out and do just that.

TYRRELL: That's right. And if, as an expert, you raise the emotional temperature, your clients become suggestible. I have seen therapists do this believing that raising emotions is automatically a good thing. People often like it because it's exciting and people mistake excitement for relevance.

YAPKO: Yes, it's dramatic but it isn't necessarily effective therapeutically. The problem we face is that, for reasons that escape me, the emotional realm of experience has attained a position at the top of the pyramid. The majority of people, including therapists, believe that there is something of more value, or more noble, about emotions. The cliché of every cartoon therapist is 'get in touch with your feelings'. There are times, with some cases, when that's an important thing to do. But, in depression for example, you sometimes need to say to them, "Get out of touch with your feelings! Get on with life. Put your feelings aside and do what needs to be done to succeed in overcoming what pains you."

When therapists, particularly in America, hear me say, "Get out of touch with your feelings", they shake their heads and roll their eyes in disbelief. It's never occurred to them that there are other elements of experience that might be more valuable in a given context.

My point is that anything can be valuable according to circumstances. Being emotionally attuned is valuable some time, some place, but so is being rational. There are times when there has to be an emotional response when spontaneity is great - but there are times when I wish a person was more structured. When I see people who don't have that sense of balance, who are continually emphasising one dimension over another, it tells me a whole lot more about them than they are telling me themselves.

TYRRELL: Can you expand on what you have said elsewhere about the effectiveness of using metaphors to bring about change - that metaphors are only appropriate in certain circumstances and not a technique that can be used with everybody. Or you say it's a question of context, it suits some people some of the time, if they latch on to the metaphor, and not on other times, when they are perhaps looking for something more concrete.

That's something I have not heard emphasised before and I was intrigued that you should do so because we are metaphorical creatures. We learn through metaphor, we enjoy the pattern in metaphorical stories right from when we are little. And metaphors are used constantly in all forms of education and the media.

YAPKO: To a certain extent, that's true. But, at the same time, consider how screwed up people are with all these highly instructive metaphors all around us from the moment we're born! We have to face it that some people don't realise something until it hits them in the forehead. They go to court, for example, and say, "I didn't know robbery was illegal." And they mean it!

The lessons of life through metaphor are all around us, but you have to be perceptive enough to pick them up. And many people just are not.

There's nothing magical about metaphors. The real artistry is in understanding how they work and the value of indirection, and then knowing your client well enough to know if they are going to respond to a particular metaphor - because everybody is different.

When you look at the cognitive literature it is clear that most people, throughout their entire lives, tend to be concrete. Metaphors on their own don't have any power. You give them power, based on your knowledge of the individual you direct them to, but there is nothing inherently powerful about them.

TYRRELL: I read some 'outcome research' somewhere that shows that more than half of inexperienced therapists get better results than trained therapists who've been practising for many years.

YAPKO: I've seen that research too, and it brings me to an interesting key distinction which is the difference between somebody who requires support and somebody who requires direction.

These are two fundamentally different needs of clients and all clients need one approach or the other in varying degrees. When I see somebody who is depressed, for example a man who has lost his wife and is really upset about it, if he says to me, "this is painful, this is going to hurt, but eventually I'll get over it. I'll go back to work. Eventually I'll remarry and my life will continue." I don't have to do anything other than support him. He's the guy I can coddle and say, "There, there. Everything will be okay." He needs *support*.

On the other hand, if he says, "I'll never fall in love again. My life is meaningless now. I don't see the point of carrying on." He needs *direction*, and that's the distinction that has to be made. When a therapist is only capable of just being a friend and being supportive he will be useless for anyone needing direction - although statistically he is bound to help a lot of people because support is all a lot of people need. But when a client needs direction and the therapist is clueless about where to go, and what to do, and how to change things, that's much harder.

A lot of people come to me desperate for help and have no idea where they are going, what they are doing, and how they are going to get there. And if I don't help them develop direction and really move them along, nothing is going to happen. Those people want me to roll up my sleeves and say, "Okay, let's get to it. Let's figure out what we've got to do here." For those people support is not going to be enough.

So that's the distinction. It's a statement about the client's needs, not about one's preferred therapeutic technique. And this issue is at the heart of the dichotomy in the field. A while back the psychotherapeutic world was awash with Carl

Rogers and the whole humanistic approach, which was strictly geared towards offering support but not direction, and in fact making the giving of direction sound like it's a big, bad thing - you're really not supposed to influence people or make value judgements - which is ridiculous!

You have to make value judgements. You disempower yourself if you don't. You've got to be able to say, "Hey! The behaviour you're engaging in is *dangerous!* You had better stop it right now. You are going to get AIDS, or your kids are going to get hurt," or whatever. And sometimes the role of the therapist isn't to comfort but to light a bonfire under their butt, and say, "Get moving!"

If someone thinks they can be a therapist without ever having to make value judgements and directing their clients, they're lost. They disempower themselves because they can't ask questions like, "What's the best response in this situation?" which is a value judgement!

TYRRELL: I am always struck by the importance of giving and receiving attention. If a client is not getting much attention in their lives, you give them some, they go away feeling great. For such people, who may be deeply depressed because of the lack of attention they are getting, you just need to point out little things like, "Why don't you go down to the pub once a week?" That alone can change their lives.

YAPKO: You're right. From being lonely and secluded he now has some beer-drinking buddies and life's great. That's how it happens.

TYRRELL: It can be as simple as that. But purposefulness also keeps people happy and sane. People who are busy and intellectually engaged in their work, tend not to get sick. Self employed people, for example, are, overall, the healthiest in the land.

I think this is because we are problem-solving animals. When we have problems that we can do something about, we don't tend to get ill, anxious and depressed. If we have problems we can do nothing about - or don't have any real problems at all - our brains fall apart (to use a technical term!).

YAPKO: That's the way the parameters fall. But I can also show you people with a strong sense of purpose and mission, who love their work and work so hard they end up with migraines, ulcers, and heart attacks at forty!

TYRRELL: They probably don't work for themselves!

YAPKO: Yes. But it's not just work. It's knowing your own limits, it's knowing what represents value for you as an individual. Balance is a key word. And it means, recognising that each thing does have a value. When you build your life around a particular value system, that value system is also your greatest vulnerability. I happen to place a huge premium on achievement, and a lot of my self-image comes from achieving. Now, what would predictably happen to me if I couldn't achieve? Supposing all of a sudden I had an accident and was in a hospital bed for three months unable to work? I'd go stark raving berserk! I'd be profoundly depressed, I know I would. And that's my vulnerability...

Medical hexing - dangerous words

Health practitioners need far more than technical ability. ***Dr Andrew Weil*** *talks to* ***Barry Winbolt*** *about a model for Integrative Medicine*

BARRY WINBOLT: You have said that, "Healing oriented medicine would serve us much better than the present system, since it would be safer and surer." You are a medical practitioner so your words can surely not be discounted with the usual arguments put up by the medical profession. Can you explain a little more about what you mean?

ANDREW WEIL: I feel that both doctors and patients need to have a great deal more confidence in the body's natural healing capabilities. This is the central piece that's missing from conventional medicine at the moment. I think that's ultimately why we're beginning to see a general crisis in healthcare around the world. We've become much too dependent on external technological interventions, and not nearly enough on the body's natural defensive processes.

WINBOLT: I know you are qualified in medicine, you were a research associate in Ethnopharmacology at Harvard, you understand the healing properties of plants and you recommend alternative treatments to your patients; but how would *you* describe yourself?

WEIL: I practise natural and preventive medicine. The term that I'm promoting in the USA is Intergrative Medicine. I don't really like either the labels alternative or complementary medicine for different reasons.

WINBOLT: Can you tell me some of those reasons?

WEIL: I think that the term alternative suggests that one is trying to replace the whole conventional system, which is not my aim. Complementary, on the other hand, sounds too weak to me. It suggests that you are trying to keep the conventional system as the centrepiece and then you have these garnishes around the edge. I want something a little less passive there. I really want to try to train people to combine the best ideas and practices of conventional and alternative medicine, and to reject the aspects that are weak, silly or nonsensical.

WINBOLT: In your latest book, *Spontaneous Healing,* you outline a new curriculum which you describe as a much-needed "radical reform of medical education." Under that heading one thing that really caught my eye was "Instruction in the art of communication," because of your use of the word 'art'.

WEIL: I have long maintained that medicine is an 'art-form science'. In the first place it uses forms of science and information produced by scientific research, but the manner of interacting with a patient is an art form; it depends on good listening and communication skills. Unfortunately these are not taught in the conventional medical system.

WINBOLT: No, they are lamentably absent. It is sad, though, isn't it, that, despite the advances we make in all sorts of areas and all the claims being made in the field of medicine, the simplest and cheapest - the way we talk to each other - is neglected.

WEIL: Yes, I find this to be an incredibly widespread problem. It's really ignorance. Most of it is not deliberate or conscious, it's just thoughtless use of words and no sense of their power. I would like to change this pattern and am working to require instruction in medical school about the power of words and the need for doctors to use extreme care in how they speak to their patients.

WINBOLT: Many people have spoken about this and it's good to hear that you are actually managing to do something about making changes. Larry Dossey wrote about what he calls modern-day Voodoo, the implantation or reinforcement of negative beliefs and expectations in patients. You call the phenomenon medical hexing.

WEIL: The patients who come to my office are highly motivated and a pleasure to work with, and they generally take responsibility for their health. They tend to be intelligent and well-educated, which is consistent with the findings of surveys of people who go to alternative practitioners. However, many of them have suffered physically, emotionally or financially as a result of their encounters with conventional medicine. Some of the stories I hear are so outrageous that all I can do is laugh; when I can get my patients to laugh as well I feel that the curses are dispelled.
WINBOLT: Hexing and cursing are powerful terms.
WEIL: Well, I can't help feeling embarrassed by my profession when I hear the many ways in which doctors convey their medical pessimism to patients, but my experience is that thoughtless medical hexing is much more common than intentional medical hexing, though it is no less harmful.
WINBOLT: There is something very insidious to it as well, quite apart from the fact that it often sets patients on a downward path that they need not take. It can actually turn them against their doctors.
WEIL: Absolutely.
WINBOLT: Often, having received a serious diagnosis, they direct their anger at their doctors, at the very time when they desperately need them. The inability of the doctors to create some empathy with those in their care alienates these patients, so they are actually reducing their own effectiveness.
WEIL: I think this is so widespread, I see it routinely in my practice in all different forms. It's not just overtly telling patients they can't get well. Another form is to say that your only course is to take this medicine for ever, for example. My feeling is that one of the most powerful things that doctors can do to promote healing is to suggest it in the language they use.
WINBOLT: You don't mince your words.
WEIL: I have had so many patients tell me these things. There is the case that I mention in the book of the wife of a

cardiac surgeon; she had very severe dermatitis and was actually contemplating suicide because it was so bad; conventional medicine had provided no real answer. She is completely healed now as a result of some fairly simple changes in lifestyle, and some supportive remedies.
WINBOLT: You mentioned it in the book, I believe, among other things you suggested she see a hypnotherapist?
WEIL: Yes, the idea frightened her at first because she didn't like the thought of anyone "taking over her mind." She followed my other recommendations regarding her diet and the addition of certain supplements and, with the early improvements in her condition and some urging, she overcame her reluctance and was pleasantly surprised. She was interviewed on a number of television programmes in the USA and she said that I was the first doctor that she had consulted who told her she could get better. In retrospect, I think that was the most valuable thing I did for her.
WINBOLT: And isn't it curious how we may say things without realising that the patient will pick up on what we assume is the most insignificant point.
WEIL: Exactly. One off-hand remark can just go right in like a little dart, and it can be either positive or negative.
WINBOLT: In your book you stress the importance of practitioners' and clients' beliefs, and we've mentioned suggestibility indirectly in terms of the way doctors speak to their patients. There is an increasing awareness of the importance of the role of the mind in healing and so fortunately there can be no real dispute as to the importance of the mind-body link. But this is fairly recent. If I look back at the books available only 20 years ago the tone and the tenor of the way these things are regarded has completely changed. Whereas, during the '70s really the only discussion was about Feldenkrais, the Alexander technique and maybe a little bit of yoga, and even then such things were only to be found in self-help books, it is now taken as read by many more people. In 20 years there has been quite an amazing

degree of progress, so, in another 20, given the way things grow exponentially, understanding of the mind-body link should at last be fairly standard.

WEIL: I'll mention to you what I see happening in the States, which I think is a model of what is going to happen elsewhere. There are two main forces at the moment that are promoting change. The first is the economic collapse of the conventional system, that's very well-known. I think the same thing is going to happen throughout the world. It's really a logical consequence of the fact that medicine made a decision this century to wed itself to technology which is inherently expensive. The bottom line is that no-one can pay these bills. We are not going to be able to legislate ourselves out of it. Hospitals are going bankrupt in the USA, and I think this is going to happen elsewhere. I go to Japan frequently and I see the same things beginning to happen in their medical system.

The other main force is the world-wide consumerist movement, in which patients are no longer satisfied with the services they are getting from doctors and so they are going elsewhere. These two powerful forces are creating a kind of desperation in medicine that is really compelling the profession to open itself to new models and new ways of doing things.

I have been asked by the University of Arizona to start a training programme. That is a measure of this desperation. They are losing customers, and since they are losing customers they cannot pay their bills.

WINBOLT: You mean the things that might have attracted people to train as doctors 20 or 30 years ago are no longer there?

WEIL: They have gone. In fact, when I talk to people here in Europe, they focus on the risk of malpractice litigation, but in a way that's minor. It's a theme, but not the major one. The big one is that, when I was in medical school, one of the great promises of medicine was that it claimed to be autonomous, you could really be your own boss. Today in the USA there are very few doctors who could make it in private practice. Most of them have to work in corporate situations, where someone above them tells them how to do it. You are told how many patients to see, and insurance companies totally dictate how medicine is done, because what's done is what's paid for and you can't deviate from that. The day-to-day practice of medicine has become more and more unsatisfying for doctors.

WINBOLT: And more and more is demanded in terms of the number of hours they put in. It is a source of constant amazement to me that what was one of the most dignified and respected professions has got itself backed into a corner where its members work such long hours and have such a high level of stress-related problems. Any other group with an organisation which protects it would be on strike! But doctors are in an invidious position and it has really gone too far. I don't know about how it is in the USA but the average GP in this country sees 155 people a week. With so much pressure and such little training of the sort we have spoken about, it is hardly surprising that their communication skills are so bad.

WEIL: Japan is the place where you can see the faults of the typical system blown up on a large screen. The average doctor there sees *30 patients an hour.* They are called two-minute doctors. They have National Health Insurance which pays 100 per cent for procedures and zero for consultations. There is no incentive for a doctor to talk to a patient and there's great incentive to do procedures. In addition, this combines with Japanese authoritarianism. You never ask a doctor a question - it's not done!

WINBOLT: So it's really taking the problem to extremes.

WEIL: Absolutely. The Japanese build all the M.R.I. scanners and the C.A.T. scanners, so every little hospital has one, and in order to get the investment back they have to use them constantly. Even if you have a pain in your knee they

do an M.R.I. scan!
WINBOLT: So the doctor is probably scribbling out notes all day, not practising healing or medicine at all, and relying on technology, rather than stimulating the body's defences.
WEIL: It is treatment rather than healing. Treatment comes from outside, healing from within.
WINBOLT: And you advocate the use of both.
WEIL: Yes. Furthermore, it is important to teach doctors and patients that when treatment works, it works because it provokes the body's healing system. It unlocks or activates healing mechanisms that are intrinsic.
WINBOLT: Which is another reason that the relationship between doctor and patient needs to be the right one regardless of the treatment used, because the right relationship can enhance the process.
WEIL: Successful patients, often those who have had life-threatening disease, frequently ally themselves to health professionals who support them in their search for answers. The practitioner has to believe in the patient's ability to heal themselves, and will empower them in their search.
WINBOLT: Speaking of empowerment, at one point in *Spontaneous Healing* you say that you do not recommend the technique of affirmations because you have no evidence that it works. Yet the work of Emile Coue in the early part of this century, based on the incantation "Every day in every way I'm getting better and better," would suggest that affirmations at least have a part to play in healing. Then, a few pages later in your book you tell the story of Rabbi Nachman, a Jewish mystic who implored his followers to "deliberately induce in themselves a buoyant, exuberant attitude towards life in order to become receptive to the subtle mysteries that surround them." He went on to say that if no inspired moments came, then they should act as if they had had them anyway. You quote him as saying, "If you have no enthusiasm, put on a front. Act enthusiastic, and the feeling will become genuine."

So you are giving an example where he is simply asking people to pretend. Is that not a kind of affirmation?
WEIL: I do not think that repeating a verbal formula is necessarily the best way to access the mind-body connection. Pretending might be better because you act out the behaviour and then it can become real.
WINBOLT: Yet, even though the type of New Age books which offer affirmations as a way to bring about therapeutic change are over-simplistic, and very often elevate tenuous links between symptoms and causes to the status of fact, quite a lot of people have found them useful - a stepping-stone to learning more about themselves and the part they play in shaping their own state of physical or mental well-being.
WEIL: I accept that. For people who are seriously ill, though, I think it is even better to seek out someone who has been healed of the condition that they have. That is a much better method than affirming to change your belief system and especially to overcome the negative programming that can occur when people believe, for example, that they cannot be helped.
WINBOLT: So it is more important for someone to get the facts about their particular condition than it is for them to simply attempt to change their negative beliefs through the kind of self-help formula made popular in recent years; "taking responsibility for one's condition" and so on.
WEIL: It is an interesting point. I really don't like this creating responsibility for illness that the New Age movement has encouraged. When I was a medical student in the late '60s, I always liked to ask people why they thought that they got an illness. At that time I saw a lot of older women with breast cancer. These were women of my grandmother's generation and the answers always were related to an old injury. They would always say things like, "Twenty years ago I fell against the kitchen table." Today though, when I ask women why they think they have breast cancer, no one mentions injury. They say things like, "I bottled up my feelings," or "I never

expressed the rage I felt towards my husband." This is a significant cultural shift. Personally I think that breast cancer is the result of complex interactions between genetics and environmental factors. There is no scientific validity to the idea that breast cancer results from an old injury. It may be that new formulations about bottled-up feelings are wrong too.

I think these new formulations make it very easy for women to then take the next step, which is to say, "therefore I gave myself cancer because somehow I failed to express feelings." If you fell against the table, that's different because there is less of a sense of personal responsibility, fate or chance or whatever.

WINBOLT: Nevertheless, attitudes, belief and expectation feature very strongly in affecting the course of serious illness. It has been shown that appraisal of one's self and approach to life can contribute significantly to the sufferer's sense of well-being. You yourself talk about imagery and seeking out the right sort of practitioners and role models, at least partly taking control of one's own health management. Working on the mind in a certain way can promote healing, and can bring about, in some cases, remission in some quite serious illnesses. So how do you make the distinction between that kind of accepting responsibility and the sort of responsibility which some people might equate with blame?

WEIL: I suppose you have to look at the consequences of that formulation. If it leads you to become paralysed by guilt, clearly it's destructive. On the other hand if it motivates you to make productive changes in your life, then that can be useful. I do believe that emotions such as grief and depression may suppress immunity, but I reject the idea that people give themselves cancer by failing to express anger and other emotions.

WINBOLT: In your book you also come out against the opposite of passivity, saying that, from your interviews with those who have experienced healing, the "I'm going to fight

this thing" attitude may not be the best way to obtain the desired result.
WEIL: This may not be the right strategy for everyone, but it seems to me that our culture promotes the fighting stance - we are comfortable with the imagery of warfare in our approaches to disease - and yet I have seen very clearly, in cases I have looked at, that the healing has more often been initiated by dropping that stance.
WINBOLT: I suppose, if you look at it as a sort of grieving process, one of the final stages of that process is acceptance.
WEIL: Exactly, acceptance is further along the healing process, and acceptance of illness is often part of a larger acceptance of self that represents a significant mental shift. Change seems more likely to occur in this climate of surrender than in a climate of confrontation with the universe.
WINBOLT: Do your medical colleagues share your views on this? The idea that we have to "beat disease" is, as you say, endemic to our society.
WEIL: I find it difficult to talk to medical scientists about this possibility because of the great gulf that exists between scientific understanding of mind-body interactions and public perceptions of the subject. In fact, relatively few of the medical establishments take the field of mind-body medicine seriously, and the most prestigious researchers, those who set priorities and influence funding, are contemptuous of it.
WINBOLT: Which makes it all the more notable that you have actually come out and declared where you stand by publishing the 'cans' and 'cannots' of allopathic medicine (Box 2). I thought you really nailed your colours to the masthead there because at the end of it you say, "Look, there are some things that allopathic medicine does really well and some things that it cannot do. Don't waste your time seeking help if it cannot do the right thing."
WEIL: One of the main things I try to do is to make both doctors and patients aware of these distinctions and that's

part of my training programme for physicians. I think they need to know when to use and when not to use the system.
WINBOLT: Is that not difficult, for some patients who are so used to going to a conventional doctor, to accept the view that medical science does not have all the answers?
WEIL: Sure, and my experience is a bit warped because I am in a very lucky position; the patients who come to see me are self-selecting. I generally see very motivated patients. I can't imagine what it would be like to work in one of these managed care facilities in the USA where the people who come in want quick fixes, where they aren't at the point where they are going to take responsibility. I love to work with motivated patients and I think, given that role, it's much easier to make patients aware of what the limitations of allopathic medicine are.
WINBOLT: It could be perceived as being irresponsible to make those sorts of recommendations to one's patients. In fact, one of the constant criticisms of complementary medicine is that people might be given advice by mistaken therapists to stay away from conventional treatment, when they may need it.
WEIL: But, you know, I see these things on both sides; it is not always down to the practitioner. There was a case I presented in the book of a man who had what turned out to be coronary pain, but he thought he had digestive pain and wasted a lot of time with complementary practitioners before he got on the right track.
WINBOLT: The quantum leap that's needed from the conventional to the non-conventional side - how do you approach it with colleagues in the medical profession who may be less receptive than you or your patients are?
WEIL: Well, I've never tried to push my ideas on people. I've been saying the same thing for 20 years and I just put the information out there. If people want to use it - fine. But increasingly, as a result of having carved out a middle position, and being quite responsible in what I recommend,

I am sought out now by large numbers of physicians and medical students who want to train with me and learn my methods.

WINBOLT: The practice of medicine provides an illusion of power you said, over life and death, and you gave a very interesting example of the type of people who might be drawn to medicine. Can you elaborate?

WEIL: Yes. I'll give you one interesting little piece of evidence for this. I once saw a survey of fatal private plane crashes in the USA. It was an analysis of the types of people who pilot small planes, and doctors overwhelmingly topped the lists of private plane pilots. In almost all of the cases these crashes had taken place in circumstances when the pilot had been advised not to fly. The author of the article attributed this to doctors' sense of omnipotence.

This is a powerful unconscious force that draws people to medicine. It's a sense of power over forces that really are not controllable.

WINBOLT: And you say this from the point of view of somebody who trains doctors.

WEIL: Yes. I think that every time a patient dies or fails to get better, it's a powerful reminder of the fact that, as a doctor, you are not in control. I suggest this as a possible reason for the medical hexing. In other words, one reason why doctors may give these negative predictions is that it is psychologically more comfortable for them; if the patients do recover they can be surprised and take credit for it, and if they don't recover they can still appear to be in control because they predicted it. Maybe this is one of the unconscious forces that leads doctors towards medical pessimism.

WINBOLT: Has no research been done into this?

WEIL: I don't know of any, but this is so common. When I talk to groups about this everyone nods their heads. The numbers of people who have been hexed is staggering! It is the rule rather than the exception. There has to be a reason for it and I'm looking for where it comes from.

WINBOLT: It's true that virtually everyone one meets has a 'horror story' regarding the way they've been told something by a doctor. You have mentioned your training programme a couple of times; are things going to change?
WEIL: I've been invited by the University of Arizona Medical Centre to start a training programme for doctors. We've called it the Programme of Intergrative Medicine (see Box 1). It will be the first US medical school with a training programme of this kind, and I think, once we break the ice, a lot of physicians will want to get in on it.
WINBOLT: How did you go about preparing the curriculum and putting the modules together? Have you delegated them to different people?
WEIL: We've formed an expert committee of 13 people, to begin thinking out a standardised curriculum. These are experts in different fields, and we had a first meeting in December 1994. One of our long range goals is to develop the model of education which can eventually be franchised out to other schools. We will have a standardised training programme and we will specifically address the problem of communication skills. The decision that we made is to require that all the people in this programme master the technique of one particular type of therapy, which I am very enthusiastic about, called Interactive Guided Imagery.
WINBOLT: So you will teach the instructors a specific technique which you feel embodies all the skills needed, rather than addressing each skill in turn?
WEIL: Yes, guided imagery depends on good rapport and good communication skills, so, rather than have people go on a course to learn communication, I think we'll just use a practical method which involves mastering these skills as part of the whole process.
WINBOLT: And so these skills will be incidental to the main subject being taught, and any errors or weaknesses of the trainees will be shown up within that context as they go along.

WEIL: Yes, the context of a practical therapy which is fun and interesting to both therapist and patient. I've seen some spectacular successes with this method.
WINBOLT: Why are you such a big fan of this type of guided imagery?
WEIL: Because it empowers patients by encouraging them to develop their own strategies for managing illness. It assumes that the unconscious mind comprehends the nature of disease processes and how to resolve them, which is consistent with the healing system's diagnostic ability. I believe that no disease is beyond the reach of these therapies and that they can enhance the effectiveness of other treatments. They should certainly be tried for all auto-immune disorders and for any illness which seems blocked or stalled.
WINBOLT: Will it be as an adjunct to conventional medical training?
WEIL: Yes. For a start it will be doctors who have completed residency training in internal medicine in family practice. This will be a two-year fellowship which is analogous to the way we train cardiologists. But the long range goal is to have this become a residency programme and to create a new field of medicine called Intergrative Medicine. Then, we hope, very long range, we'll be able to drop the adjective and this will be the Medicine of the future.

The Medical Training Curriculum

ALL PREVIOUS attempts to modify the medical training curriculum have done little to address the real needs. To remedy this Dr Andrew Weil proposes:

- Basic instruction in the philosophy of science, with reference to new models based on quantum physics that replace old concepts of Newtonian mechanism and Cartesian dualism. Such instruction would include information on probability and discussion of possible interactions of the observer and the observed, and presentation of models that could account for non-physical causes of physical events.
- Instruction in the history of medicine with reference to the development of major systems like traditional Chinese medicine, homeopathy, and osteopathy.
- Emphasis on the healing power of nature and the body's healing system.
- Emphasis on mind/body interactions, including placebo responses, medical hexing, and psychoneuroimmunology.
- Instruction in psychology and spirituality in addition to information about the physical body.
- Reduction in the amount of factual knowledge students are now required to memorise to pass certifying examinations. If students learn how to learn, and know the general structure of knowledge in the various medical sciences, they will be able to look up the details as they need them, especially as this information becomes available in computerised formats.
- Provision of practical experience in the areas of nutrition, exercise, relaxation, meditation, and visualisation. Students should be evaluated not only on factual knowledge but on personal progress in developing healthy lifestyles.
- Practical experience with the basic techniques of alternative medicine, such as herbalism, nutritional medicine, manipulation, body work, breath work, acupuncture, and guided imagery, in addition to the basic techniques of allopathic medicine.
- Instruction on how to design and conduct research in medicine and how to evaluate published research.
- Instruction in the art of communication, including interviewing patients, taking medical histories, and presenting treatments in ways that are likely to activate the body's healing system.

Reproduced from Spontaneous Healing, *published by Little Brown, London.*

Box 1

Allopathic medicine

Dr Andrew Weil's summary of what he says allopathic medicine can and cannot do:

Allopathic medicine can:
Manage trauma better than any other system of medicine;
Diagnose and treat many medical and surgical emergencies;
Treat acute bacterial infections with antibiotics;
Treat some parasitic and fungal infections;
Prevent many infectious diseases by immunisation;
Diagnose complex medical problems;
Replace damaged hips and knees;
Get good results with cosmetic and reconstructive surgery;
Diagnose and correct hormonal deficiencies.

It cannot:
Treat viral infections;
Cure most chronic degenerative diseases;
Effectively manage most kinds of mental illness;
Cure most forms of allergy or auto-immune disease;
Effectively manage psychosomatic illnesses;
Cure most forms of cancer.

He also says: "Do not seek help from a conventional doctor for a condition that conventional medicine cannot treat, and do not rely on an alternative provider for a condition that conventional medicine can manage well. "

Reproduced from *Spontaneous Healing*, published by Little Brown, London,

Box 2

Why hypnosis and the power of the mind matter in medicine

*In the 1930s, a Bedouin tribesman introduced a young Irish doctor to the powers of the subconscious mind. Sixty years later, after doing over four thousand operations using hypnosis, **Dr Jack Gibson** talks to **Joe Griffin**.*

JOE GRIFFIN: Can I take you back to the beginning, how you became interested in hypnosis because when you qualified as a surgeon it wasn't part of the curriculum.
Dr JACK GIBSON: When I was a boy there was a clergyman who used hypnosis for people who were getting seasick and he cured them. I was most impressed by him. Later on when I took up medicine I went to my professor, I told him about hypnosis and he told me that no doctor uses hypnosis, it is only used by quacks. In the Channel Islands a few years later I watched a stage hypnosis show and I saw the possibilities. I asked a psychiatrist if hypnosis could be used to treat an asthma case. He said he could do it himself. He took the asthma case into a mental hospital, the doors were locked, the relatives weren't allowed to see the patient for three days and the patient came back a wreck.
GRIFFIN: He was allegedly using hypnosis?
GIBSON: I suppose he knew a bit about it but he didn't know much. It was while practising surgery in the Middle East as a young graduate that I first encountered the beneficial effect of the controlled use of the subconscious mind. A Bedouin tribesman had a growth on his leg which tracked down between the muscles. He knew it would have to be removed. But he said "I won't have any anaesthetic". I offered him a local anaesthetic but he refused it. As I operated on him, I myself felt that he must be suffering great pain. I actually felt the pain myself. When the operation was over, he said, calmly, "May I see it before you put the dressing on". It was

only later when I learned to operate with hypnosis myself that I realised that he hadn't suffered any pain at all. Then, later on, I was in Africa, about 36 years ago, I was in a practice there, I was the surgical part of the practice. I went to see a man who had a bad chest, his bed was burnt from going to sleep smoking a cigarette at night. I was afraid of him setting the house on fire, for he had children in the house and it was a long way from anyone. I thought the children could be burnt to death. So I thought I'd hypnotise him, he was my first case. He went very deep. I was thrilled by it, and after that I got into it in a big way.

GRIFFIN: Did he stop smoking?

GIBSON: I don't know. He responded to my posthypnotic suggestions and I took it for granted he'd stop. I knew nothing about hypnosis then. Nowadays I would get him to confirm that he had stopped.

GRIFFIN: So that was your first case!

GIBSON: Then, only three days later, a person rang up. She had a paralysed leg and I suspected it was psychosomatic. So I went out to see her and, sure enough, it was. She got over it in about half an hour. I had enough sense to try to get her to face up to the things that made her leg paralysed.

GRIFFIN: So you were doing psychotherapy as well as hypnosis from that point?

GIBSON: Yes. And she was going to have a baby and she had the baby under hypnosis. It was absolutely marvellous.

GRIFFIN: That was some time later?

GIBSON: That was about a fortnight later.

GRIFFIN: So, you'd established your credentials with her by getting her leg cured?

GIBSON: Yes. After that I used hypnotherapy whenever possible. Later I came back to Ireland and took up a job as a surgeon in the hospital, here in Naas, and a very busy practice it was too.

GRIFFIN: What was the reaction of the doctors here in the hospital when they saw you using hypnosis?

GIBSON: Positive. I had no complaints in twenty years of working.
GRIFFIN: So they had an open-minded attitude to it, even using hypnosis as an anaesthetic?
GIBSON: Yes.
GRIFFIN: So how many operations do you think you've performed using hypnosis as an anaesthetic?
GIBSON: Over four thousand, but that includes all the simple operations as well. I used it all of the time, for dislocations, for fractures, for people injured in car accidents. Very often they would have had a meal beforehand and of course then, to use anaesthetics, we'd have had to wait a long time for the stomach to empty but, with hypnosis, I could work straight away.
GRIFFIN: Do you think that saved the hospital money?
GIBSON: The amount of money saved was enormous.
GRIFFIN: Yes. I was wondering about that. In terms of theatre time and keeping people longer in bed and having more doctors involved.
GIBSON: But they never considered that.
GRIFFIN: Something that would be very relevant today, don't you think, when all the state medical services are overburdened financially?
GIBSON: Well, they could cut down expenses tremendously. You take a fractured nose, admit to hospital, operate the next day. Whereas I would just take the fellow and hypnotise him and give it a push to straighten it, put on a splint to keep it in place, and then let him home. The cost would be a fraction of the cost of an admission.
GRIFFIN: So do you see a case for doctors and anaesthetists being actually trained in hypnosis and using it?
GIBSON: I think all doctors and anaesthetists should be trained in the use of hypnosis.
GRIFFIN: What do you think stops that happening?
GIBSON: Prejudice!
GRIFFIN: What do you think is the source of that prejudice?

GIBSON: Money!
GRIFFIN: It is not in some people's financial interests to use hypnosis.
GIBSON: I have trained doctors here and they don't use it. If they went into a surgery and there were twenty people there and each of them willing to pay for treatment, and if they were to take the people out who needed hypnotherapy and give them an hour or an hour and a half they would obviously see fewer patients and therefore earn less money. But what they don't realise in the national health service where people are paid so much per year, if they treated an asthma case they'd get better and they'd save an awful lot of money and save a lot of time.
GRIFFIN: So you found asthma responds well to hypnosis?
GIBSON: Absolutely. Dramatically.
GRIFFIN: Is this particular types of asthma?
GIBSON: All cases of asthma, particularly with children.
GRIFFIN: There was an anecdote in your book about you once being invited to see what you could do for a hospital ward full of children suffering from asthma. The children stayed there an average of six months. All the children you worked with responded really well to hypnosis. Yet you were asked to discontinue your work by the hospital authorities.
GIBSON: Yes. They thought I was using magic. There is probably no condition among children which is so easy to treat with self hypnosis. I have found that most asthmatics lose their attacks almost right away, their lives transformed in the process. Sometimes the attacks stop with the child's first lesson in relaxation. To help the child (or an adult) to learn how to relax in the event of another attack a self-hypnosis tape is very useful. If the child has learned to relax listening to the tape, then in the event of an attack it is relatively easy for the child to relax listening to the tape and let the spasm pass. In my view, having dealt with many asthmatic cases, there is one factor common to all allergies and that factor is subconscious fear. It is only in the reaching

of the subconscious mind, with the erasure of the erroneous information stored there and its replacement with the true facts, that a cure will be effected. When an asthmatic attack occurs fear causes the muscles in the lungs to go into spasm, but if a child has learned how to relax, the first thing he must think about is relaxing and then the fear will go, and with it the asthmatic attack. So that in time he becomes free from asthma.

GRIFFIN: More generally, would you see hypnotherapy as an effective treatment mode for many illnesses?

GIBSON: I believe hypnosis to be as effective as antibiotics. Of course, antibiotics will cure diseases which hypnosis cannot help, but hypnosis can cure cases where antibiotics are of no use whatsoever.

GRIFFIN: Can you expand on that?

GIBSON: If any doctor were to practise without using antibiotics he would risk being struck off the medical register - many of his patients would die unnecessarily without their use. Yet, if one who had used hypnosis were faced with the choice of whether he should give up using antibiotics or hypnosis, he would be faced with a difficult choice. At first sight it might appear that antibiotics are, beyond question, the more important. Yet antibiotics, unlike hypnosis, can touch only a small proportion of human suffering. When penicillin was first discovered, a small batch was sent to the north of England for experimental use, no one seemed to believe in it and it lay there unused. Consequently, even though a relatively junior surgeon, I was allowed to make the first trial and I injected it into a septic hip joint. The result was dramatic and I have prescribed antibiotics ever since. I believe that shutting one's eyes to the use of hypnotherapy is as unscientific as the shutting of eyes then was to the possible use of penicillin. That's because, if they are closed to the fact that there is access to the subconscious mind, we will continue to treat patients symptomatically with such things as tranquillisers, sleeping tablets, bronchial

dilators and so on, instead of aiming at curing the root cause of the complaints.
GRIFFIN: How can hypnosis help one to find that root cause?
GIBSON: The nervous system is composed of the voluntary and autonomic nervous system. The autonomic system is controlled by the subconscious mind. Hypnosis gives access to the subconscious mind. If we, as doctors, do not accept this fact then we are cowboys. Cowboys without lassoes, for if we cannot catch this elusive beast, we will continue to see the appalling unnecessary suffering and death from readily curable psychosomatic diseases.
GRIFFIN: The other side of all this is that, if people respond so well to suggestion, then presumably influential figures like doctors in their practice may be giving what are, in effect, hypnotic suggestions, but may not be aware they're giving them when they are offering a prognosis on an illness. For example, when the doctor casually says 'we are talking here about months rather than years', the patient may take that as gospel, he may take it as a form of hypnotic suggestion and actually die on cue.
GIBSON: It's true.
GRIFFIN: So perhaps part of the education process that is needed is for all healthcare personnel to be aware of the power of suggestion, both negative and positive.
GIBSON: Yes. We've need to be *very* aware of that.
GRIFFIN: You on your part must be unique in having performed over four thousand operations, major and minor, using hypnosis. Probably very few doctors in the world could claim to have had that much experience with the medical use of hypnosis .
GIBSON: Except of course with acupuncture in China. Acupuncture, I think, is hypnosis being used.
GRIFFIN: That's interesting. I saw some research done by two doctors in the states called Spiegel and Spiegel and they found that the subjects who responded well to acupuncture also respond well to hypnosis. They also speculated that

acupuncture is a form of hypnotic induction.
GIBSON: It is. About thirty years ago a Mr Chance, a great orthopaedic consultant here in Ireland, was very taken with hypnosis and he advised me to use it but added "for goodness sake give them an injection at the same time, it doesn't matter if it's only vitamin B or water, let them feel the injection does it". I couldn't do that, I didn't think it was honest. The acupuncture people have a needle and they jab the needle in. The acupuncturist is convinced it works, the patients are convinced it works, the hospital is convinced it works - and so it *does* work.
GRIFFIN: But *why* it works is another matter.
GIBSON: They can put the needles in sites other than the official sites and it still works. Or they can use electrical wires to simulate the acupuncture and get even better results. Their success rate is very similar to that of pure hypnosis.
GRIFFIN: Since you have raised the issue, can I ask you when you were using hypnosis in surgery what proportion of patients would respond to hypnosis?
GIBSON: That's a question I find hard to answer as I kept no notes. There is a difference between a cold case and an emergency. If I said to you, "will you have this finger off under hypnosis or a general anaesthetic" almost for certain you would say a general anaesthetic, and if I tried to hypnotise you, it wouldn't work. But if you came into hospital with your finger bleeding and your stomach full and there is no way we can operate on you for some time, you would accept hypnosis. I think we have a high rate of patients under those conditions who are good subjects.
GRIFFIN: What is your preferred method of inducing the anaesthesia? Is it a distraction technique or telling them that their hand will go numb?
GIBSON: I will start from the beginning.

I pick up the hand very gently. I tell them "If you relax you will feel less pain. And if you relax very deeply, you may actually feel no pain at all". I then, holding the arm in the gentlest way, wash around the wound with an antiseptic such as iodine which can cause pain, but I am very careful not to let a drop fall into the wound. Then I get an antiseptic that doesn't hurt and gently put it into the wound. But the whole time I'm telling them, "if you relax, it will help you. Relax deeper and deeper". And then when I start to stitch, I pick up a needle I say to them "I can give you an injection now and you won't feel any pain but the injection won't take the pain away completely because when the effect wears off you will feel the pain again. But if you relax deeply enough for the stitching not to be felt it will be grand. I can stitch the wound then you will have no pain and no pain afterwards".

By this time the person is probably hypnotised. I can pick out any pieces of dirt that are in the wound without causing pain. Now the person is becoming deeply hypnotised and I can dispense with the anaesthetic and put in a stitch and they won't feel any pain at all. At the same time it may be necessary to cut the edges of the wound off to make them even and less ragged. This will be done without any pain whatsoever.

When I have finished the stitching, the person is feeling very well. They have enjoyed, actually enjoyed the feeling of the arm being numb and the wound being stitched. They will accept the feeling of being free from pain and even be free from pain later on when the stitches are removed.

GRIFFIN: That really does help to clarify the way you induce anaesthesia with hypnosis.

GIBSON: When I was in Vienna last year I went out to dinner with friends. There was a man there who didn't know anything about hypnosis. A colleague asked me to explain to him how I stitched a wound using hypnosis. I took his hand very gently and I worked with him. When I'd finished, my colleague said "look at him, his hand is up in the air and he can't put it down". I had to tell him "your arm is free".

GRIFFIN: Have you heard about Dr. Escudero in Spain? I have heard he uses a technique involving the use of saliva to

produce anaesthesia.
GIBSON: There is only one way and that is by getting the person to relax. He has a hospital where everybody is keyed up to do this one thing and he believes it, the patients believe it, the hospital, of course, believes it, and it works. In his method the mouth must be wet, if the mouth is wet the person isn't terrified. If you were terrified it would be dry.

Witch doctors used the same technique in Africa. If a man committed a murder, say, the witch doctor would get all the men in the village to line up. They all believed he had magic powers, and he would go around with a hot poker and touch all of their tongues and the murders' tongue would be burnt because his mouth was dry. Those with wet tongues wouldn't have any pain.
GRIFFIN: When you retired as a surgeon you then went into hypnotherapy practise treating psychotherapy patients. Wasn't that a big change?
GIBSON: Yes, it was a big change, but remember, I retired at the age of seventy, I *had* to retire anyway, but by then I had so many hypnotherapy cases I was glad to. For the previous twenty years I had practised both surgery *and* hypnotherapy.
GRIFFIN: I want to ask you where did your expertise in understanding human nature come from? That's a completely different field from being a surgeon.
GIBSON: Very few have much understanding of human nature, or the ability to share compassion. I suppose I always was interested in people.
GRIFFIN: I am interested in the approach you take to the different types of complaints and illnesses as outlined in your book and tapes. I was impressed by your creative use of language and suggestion and the psychological insights that you use. It seems to me they must have come from a lot of reflection but also there must have been some sources for this insight and knowledge.
GIBSON: I think most of it came from my religion. There was a man called Lesley Weatherhead who wrote many books, I

was interested in what he did.
GRIFFIN: He explored the mind from a psychological philosophical and religious perspective. You drew inspiration from his books?
GIBSON: Yes and from himself.
GRIFFIN: In what way from himself?
GIBSON: I went to hear him preaching. I was spellbound.
GRIFFIN: Do you suppose he was a bit of a hypnotist?
GIBSON: Well, I suppose every good preacher is really.
GRIFFIN: Do you think that religious views, or at least a commitment to something beyond oneself, is important in mental health?
GIBSON: If they are truly religious!
GRIFFIN: How would you make that distinction?
GIBSON: Some people are religious but they don't believe in the truth, not in their lives.
GRIFFIN: What do you think is the fundamental religious truth?
GIBSON: I'm not particularly religious in the terms of orthodox or any other kind of religion. I believe the world was born with a big bang. I don't know if all we are told is true.
GRIFFIN: Do you suppose that there is a deeper pattern that somehow connects human beings and that religion, historically, has tried to encapsulate and express that, and that one doesn't have to be a member of a formal religion to be aware or have a sense of this pattern?
GIBSON: Yes.
GRIFFIN: I believe you were the first person to make a self hypnosis record.
GIBSON: I'd be interested in finding out. I think I was the first - in about the late 1950s. It was for treating any condition but mainly asthma, but I didn't sell them. But in 1962 I made an EP and sold it, and then, when cassette tapes came out, I recorded on them. In 1970 my *Stop Smoking* recording was top of the pops in Ireland for six weeks running.

GRIFFIN: Alternative therapies are becoming increasingly popular. Do you think this reflects some inadequacies in the medical model and how it's being applied in practice?
GIBSON: I think we are far too slow in taking on the fact that we have a subconscious mind. When I gave my lecture to the Medical Society at University College Dublin, I said that the medical profession was influenced by body snatchers and we learnt about how the body works. But the dead body has no mind. And still today we spend years teaching how the body works but only a few minutes teaching how the mind works. We need to realise that the mind is just as important as the body.

Very early on in my career, I found that I had been very well taught in the physical side of medicine, but had received almost no training in the causes or treatment of most of the illness I met in practice. We were taught to treat asthma with cortisone and bronchial dilators. I saw the attacks disappear for a time but they nearly always returned. I gave painkillers to migraine suffers but their migraine returned. I treated insomniacs with sedatives but none were cured of the underlying cause of their inability to sleep. I saw the addicts of drugs, alcohol and nicotine listen to my advice only to reject it. This led me to realise just how much of human misery has its origins in the mind. To get to the root of the problem we have to be able to tap into the power of the subconscious mind and to release the faulty learnings often contained there.
GRIFFIN: So doctors have to be able to learn to tap into the power of the mind.
GIBSON: And that's where we've gone wrong. We haven't done that.
GRIFFIN: Take a doctor seeing one hundred and twenty five or more patients in a week - would it be practicable to expect him to be able to utilise that knowledge?
GIBSON: We don't have enough doctors to treat everybody. Just having a number of people treating the physical illness

is not enough. We've got to have people treating the mental side as well. There's far greater need on the mental than on the physical side. More people are in hospital who are suffering from a psychosomatic illness than from a physical illness.

GRIFFIN: What illnesses would you classify as psychosomatic?

GIBSON: Well, take all the mental hospitals: there are more people in the mental hospitals than there are in the general hospitals. In the general hospital there are a lot of people injured in accidents caused by alcohol abuse, people dying through the effects of smoking and other drugs, and illnesses caused by stress. So if we broke down the physical illnesses the majority of them could even be seen as psychosomatically caused.

GRIFFIN: You'll be interested in the report in the report published in *The Therapist* on various methods of getting people to stop smoking, including the patch, and it was found that hypnotherapy was easily the most effective.

GIBSON: I get most people to stop without withdrawal symptoms, although I don't promise that. But I notice that those who are really keen very often stop without any withdrawal symptoms.

If someone knows that smoking is likely to cause them a great deal of suffering, but still retains reservations about quitting, then it is not nearly so easy. It's important to have sincerity of intention because this makes reaching into the emotions and achieving harmony proportionally easier. But if one has honestly decided not to take nicotine again than this thought can be transferred to the subconscious mind and very often the person can stop smoking without withdrawal symptoms.

GRIFFIN: So the very fact that they are highly motivated, combined with suggestions from you telling them that they are going to feel comfortable and relaxed and confident as non-smokers, is sufficient to generate the ability to be free

from cigarettes without the withdrawal symptoms. That's an amazing relief from suffering.
GIBSON: Absolutely! My daughter gave up smoking. She wouldn't come to me. People don't go to their relatives, but it's three years now and she's still got the withdrawal symptoms.
GRIFFIN: I notice in your book you are also quite optimistic about helping people with obesity, that you feel that hypnotherapy can help them to lose weight successfully.
GIBSON: Losing weight is different. Smoking - we can forget about it, but we can't forget eating. We have to have consistency. If a person wants to lose four stone they have got to think in terms of a couple of years and not to think of it happening in a few months. If they think of it as a long-term thing they can learn to gradually reduce and enjoy their food more than they are enjoying it now. An overweight person doesn't usually enjoy food as a rule. Some do but most don't.
GRIFFIN: That's because the feel so guilty.
GIBSON: Yes because they feel guilt. If they would eat reasonable amounts and stop when they are no longer hungry they would lose weight, and there is no other way in which it can be done. Reducing weight in this way does not strain the will as other dieting methods tend to do. With relaxation and mind control, the whole being is in harmony in the intention to lose weight.
GRIFFIN: I was also very impressed as to how you helped people with drink problems, because there you actually did some research into the problem as to the best approach and actually worked and researched with alcoholics as to what would be the most effective way of doing it.
GIBSON: They used to come here and sit in the evening, the alcoholics, some of their relatives and some of the people who treated them. The alcoholics tore my self hypnosis record to pieces week after week, but I kept on going until they said they were satisfied with it, and that had it been available earlier it could have saved them years of hell.

GRIFFIN: You had the alcoholics fantasise in hypnosis going for a drink!?

GIBSON: Yes. They loved that part. The part where they relaxed and imagined themselves drinking, tasting their favourite tipple and feeling all those sensations of release, entering as it were another world, a world of happiness and then returning home the money still in their pockets, with the feelings of remorse replaced by one of tranquillity. This turned out to be the most important part of the cassette. For the greatest thing that alcoholics wish to achieve is a feeling of contentment that is not gained through drinking.

GRIFFIN: So the cassette showed them they could create the same sense of release through self hypnosis as they previously got through drink.

GRIFFIN: I understand you were in Lithuania last year?

GIBSON: Yes, I read an appeal that they wanted books on hypnotherapy and I went out there. I gave them copies of my book and tapes and did some demonstrations.

GRIFFIN: Was there a language problem?

GIBSON: I worked through an interpreter and they all went under.

GRIFFIN: What are your plans for the future?

GIBSON: I plan to write a book on hypnosis in surgery. For my background research I intend to travel to China and Spain to study their methods of working without chemical anaesthetics. That should make an interesting chapter.

GRIFFIN: A new chapter in an interesting and productive life. I wish you luck with your new writing and I'm sure it will help to increase public and health service awareness of the value of hypnosis, properly used, in the treatment of illness.

Freud's labyrinth of error

Richard Webster, *author of 'Why Freud Was Wrong', has done more to lift the dank spell Freud cast over 20th century minds than any other researcher. He talks here with* ***Pat Williams*** *about how Freud, after reawakening Europe to the unconscious, then went on to cripple the development of psychotherapy.*

PAT WILLIAMS: Have you been psychoanalysed?
RICHARD WEBSTER: No, I haven't. I'm not a refugee from therapy. I suppose it would be true to say that it is Sigmund Freud's influence on our culture which really interests me. Chiefly because I have come to see that, although many aspects of Freud's work appear to be full of insights, and in many respects Freud seemed the kind of cultural prophet we needed to get us out of a certain kind of Victorian prudery, this is an illusion. Freud was profoundly mistaken in all manner of ways.
WILLIAMS: As you make clear in your excellent book, some of that was because of the medical misconceptions of the time. Freud saw as psychogenic all sorts of conditions we now know are brain lesions or epilepsies, and treated the unfortunate sufferers as if they had traumas laid down in early childhood! Brainwashed them, you might say, into accepting nonexistent psychological traumas. Thus adding to, not lessening, their load.
WEBSTER: Yes, he was drawn deeper and deeper into a labyrinth of error from which he never escaped. But it is not helpful to say Freud removed the veils from the realm of the obscene - for the simple reason that in many respects that actually inverts Freud's significance. He successfully persuaded the culture at large he was doing that, while at the same time concealing a deeper mission, much more attuned to the central ideals of the Judaeo-Christian tradition. That is really where we must situate Freud. He was in many respects deeply traditional, deeply puritanical,

and deeply hostile to the very kinds of sexual behaviour he was seen as affirming.

WILLIAMS: It has always seemed to me that it was Freud who reminded the culture at large that there are many things in our minds of which we are unconscious. That knowledge had always existed in certain individuals and certain cultures, but not ours and not then. A.A. Brill, a psychoanalyst who worked with Freud, said: 'It had never occurred to me before I studied psychoanalysis that it was possible to obtain any information about a patient which transcended his own conscious knowledge. But after some experience with free associations and interpretation, I became convinced that the average person is as ignorant of the mental forces behind his thoughts and actions as is a traveller of the motive powers that propel the aeroplane, motorcar or train that hurries to some appointed place.' That genuinely astonished reaction, that feeling that psychoanalysis had blown the gaffe, that amazement that what you saw was not necessarily what was there . . . illustrates well the general perception in the culture at the time.

WEBSTER: Yes. But an awareness of unconscious forces had always been there - you find it in Shakespeare, you find it in Greek times. It is a misunderstanding to believe this was Freud's great discovery. Freud was a neurologist, trained in medicine, and the medical ideas which he brought to psychoanalysis remain crucial to it throughout its development. We forget it was born as a medical movement and remained a medical movement in its deepest thinking.

It's most important to understand that what Freud discovered, or thought he had discovered, was not unconscious motivation. It was the unconscious generation of physical symptoms. In other words his concept of the unconscious was not something which was there primarily to allow us to understand the complexities of ordinary human behaviour; it was there to allow us to understand how certain physical symptoms were formed. And, unless we understand that Freud's concept of the unconscious was crucially to do with the unconscious as a pathogenic source, we don't understand psychoanalysis. We reconstruct psychoanalysis in a humanistic image - the kind of thing we would like it to have been! And by doing that we make it much more interesting, fertile, potentially rich a thing than it actually was or ever could become.

WILLIAMS: Mmm. Years ago I was meeting many analysts and analysands, and I also read widely on the subject. I remember clearly the actual smell, the dank whiff of psychoanalysis, when people spoke or wrote of it. It all seemed so narrow and claustrophobic and cramping, that instinct kept me clear of it. As you say, anything but rich and fertile!

WEBSTER: That's a very interesting way of putting it. In some ways my experience was the opposite. I found the smell interesting at first. You think 'yes', but then, when you get inside it, you realise there's no way out.

WILLIAMS: It's absolutely smothering.

WEBSTER: You're trapped within a sort of church. Churches smell wonderfully of incense, but when you go in to savour the incense you suddenly find that you've got the ten commandments hanging over your head.

WILLIAMS: Freud as Old Testament Prophet! As you say in your book, he had a Messianic certainty, that his work was intended to be on an almost religious scale. But you pointed out earlier that he's working at a time where neurology knows very little. And it's easy to make mistakes if you theorise in the absence of real information.

WEBSTER: Yes, neurologists then thought they knew almost everything but didn't actually know very much. At the time Freud came to Paris to study under Charcot, towards the end of Charcot's career, the dangerous delusion of having solved all the major neurological problems was more or less in position. One thing we can say about medical progress is that people always underestimate the depths of medical ignorance, and always think that the dry land of certain knowledge is within reach. The degree of diagnostic darkness was extreme at the end of the nineteenth century. It was very easy to misconstrue some of the subtler unidentified neurological disorders as psychosomatic or psychological or psychogenic in some way. Freud tended to do this, certainly at the beginning of his career, when he was laying the foundations of psychoanalysis. He was deeply confused by this diagnostic darkness.

WILLIAMS: You actually give in your book examples of the consequences of this kind of theorising in the dark. For those who perhaps don't know this material, can you give an example?

WEBSTER: Perhaps the most interesting case of all is not Freud's, it is Breuer's - the case of Anna 0 - but which has always been seen, and was seen by Freud, as the founding case of psychoanalysis. Anna 0 suffered from extraordinary disabling physical symptoms, including contractures, paralysis, as well as many other symptoms such as the appearance of a sort of double personality. I had always taken for granted that Anna 0 was indeed suffering a genuine psychological illness. When you come across one of the most curious of her symptoms, that she had forgotten or was unable at certain points to speak her native language, and could only speak in a form of 'telegram English' or 'telegram German', you think this is clearly psychological. But of course that merely reflects our own ignorance of neuropathology,

Anna O's case was a revelation to me, and trying to understand it changed the entire shape of my book. I read the account of Anna O's illness by Elizabeth Thornton, that most neglected and abused of Freud scholars and the one who has come up with some of the most valuable insights. In *The Freudian Fallacy,* originally published under the title *Freud and Cocaine,* Thornton, a medical historian with her own knowledge of modern neurological discoveries, looked again at Anna 0 and pointed to some extraordinarily clear resemblances between her symptoms and certain neurological disorders.

What was so attractive about her account was that it had explanatory power. There were all kinds of details which I had tended to cast aside and say well I don't understand that. But her reading of the case of Anna 0 suddenly made you realise that all these things which you had wanted to dismiss as insignificant because you didn't understand them, were actually keys to understanding her illness. That was what made me realise that, in order to understand Freud, you have to go much deeper into the medical context.

I had to learn a great deal about neurology, about what we have discovered and how recently, sometimes, we have discovered it. For example, something like frontal lobe epilepsy, which actually bears an extraordinary resemblance to what Charcot was describing as hysteria, was only really recognised as late as the 1980s. Even temporal lobe epilepsy wasn't fully recognised until the 1930s.

Having discovered all this, I also discovered the immense scepticism of many people towards this reading of Anna O's case. Most psychoanalysts were obviously not impressed, but even people trained in general medicine or as neurologists, were sometimes extremely reluctant to accept it. Then I found that not only Elizabeth Thornton, but a number of other people had written very similar accounts in which they had quite independently pointed to the same phenomena. That made me realise that Thornton had uncovered something very interesting. Though we may never be certain, Anna 0 was probably suffering from a form of encephalitis or related neurological disorder.

WILLIAMS: The medical authoritarianism of the day is still with us! But Charcot and Freud seem to have been these great 'I-ams', refusing to let anything simply be, without deciding what it was. They were chopping off toes and heels to make all feet fit the same shoe.

WEBSTER: Yes. I think that's so, but there is something else also. Having misconstrued certain organic symptoms which were really symptoms of genuine illnesses, and having perceived those symptoms as actually psychogenic, Freud then turned that round and looked at people's emotional problems. What I'm trying to say is that, having seen a real organic illness as something psychologically induced, he then reasoned backwards and said that, if somebody had an emotional problem, then it was really an illness.

WILLIAMS: In the cliche of film, a character behaves unacceptably or criminally, and another character says in tones of contempt: 'You're sick!' That's how far this point of view has reached! But you also relate this driving need to produce a systematic and comprehensive explanation of all psychogenic, was thought to be psychogenic, symptoms, to Freud's need for fame; his deep conviction of his special mission. You sound this theme early in your book, and constantly return to it.

WEBSTER: Other biographers have noted this in passing. But because they were not really seeking to understand Freud's motivation, they haven't always given these things enough attention. I became fascinated because it seemed to me that the resemblance between the entire pattern of life and the pattern of the lives of traditional leaders is extraordinarily close.

I wondered what might have created this in his childhood. Some people have said, well look here, this kind of close investigation of somebody's childhood is the essence of psychoanalysis! They say that one of the most revealing parts of my book is where I talk about Freud's childhood and development because, by doing so, I am showing how valuable psychoanalysis is. But that shows how much we have re-invented psychoanalysis, because one of the things Freud simply was not interested in, and this is something that we find great difficulty coming to terms with, was the intricacies and complexities of the emotional relationship which develops between parents and children.

WILLIAMS: And now you *really* surprise me.

WEBSTER: Let me put it in another way. Freud was really

only interested in the relationships which, according to his own reductive biological model, ought to exist between parents and children. What people *actually* did and what they said that they felt - which is to say the larger part of human behaviour - didn't fit into this model. It was irrelevant. My own interest in Freud's motivation is certainly a non-Freudian interest. The way I saw Freud was as somebody who experienced, when he was young, great adulation from his parents. He was born with a caul, and this was seen by them as a portent of greatness. Throughout his life he was the golden boy who was going to have great academic glory. It was a time when Jewish messianic hope had gone to some extent underground, but where it was still the heart of the culture.

One can see certain ways in which the huge expectations which Freud's parents had of him became intertwined with their own perception of him as a great man. And somehow Freud knew he had to be a great man to retain his parents' affection. This was his predicament. He was the messiah waiting for a revelation which never seemed to come. And, at a certain point in his life, he became desperate. There he was, absolutely certain of his future glory and yet still with no doctrine to dispense to bring that about. At a certain point the acuteness of this messianic dilemma, this desperation, made it impossible for him to interrogate sceptically any idea under whose spell he came. Cocaine was his first candidate for the world redeeming panacea, the medicine which would somehow transform the universe. As the discoverer of cocaine he would be the bringer of a particular kind ecological gospel to mankind.

But so enraptured was Freud by what he thought was his discovery, that he failed to note the addictive effects of cocaine when he used it to wean his friend from morphine! It only happened because Freud fell credulously in love with an idea which seemed to have some world-redeeming power. That was the first instance of the repeating pattern. The perceived

version of Freud's life is that the cocaine disaster was the great aberration. The young man was rash and after that he learned, and was then much more cautious and sensible when he created psychoanalysis. Well, of course, this is a good way to explain away the cocaine disaster.
WILLIAMS: But this happened over and over again, fuelled by his need to find his 'message'.
WEBSTER: Well, some people say that Freud consciously, deliberately and fraudulently falsified, but I think that idea is based on a fundamental misconception.
WILLIAMS: More like a pattern driven by a need to achieve than conscious fraud?
WEBSTER: Yes, I think that what some people don't understand is the capacity we all have, and particularly messianic characters like Freud have, for self deception They are not doing it on purpose, so I take issue with the view of Freud as a complete fraud. He was not a confidence trickster, as Peter Medawar described him, deliberately setting out to deceive others. Freud was passionately convinced he had found the truth. And he felt that so deeply that he was led again and again to protect what he saw as an immensely valuable idea against anything which might prevent us from enjoying its benefits. So I think he was actually being protective towards a system he saw as so valuable that he couldn't let 'minor objections' stand in the way.
WILLIAMS: You are actually describing the sort of thinking which leads to cults.
WEBSTER: Yes. Though I would be slightly reluctant to accept the word cult, because I think that what Freud created was something much greater than that. In a way, a cult is something we see as a sort of minor aberration from a religious tradition.
WILLIAMS: Cult behaviour can be found in many places, and many of them very respectable.
WEBSTER: I accept that. I would just want to emphasise that the cultic aspects of psychoanalysis were profoundly

similar to the cultic aspects of the early Christian movement, and that, in many respects, what Freud founded was a cult which came directly out of that tradition. It had the same largeness of aspiration and, indeed, in the end was successful almost in the same way. It was a way of reconstructing in a disguised secular form the central and most important orthodoxies of the Judaeo-Christian faith, and presenting them in a way that they would not be challenged by science precisely because they were presented as science.

So I want to stress Freud's cultural centrality and his orthodoxy by pointing to the way in which he stood in a kind of line of succession which led back to the great thinkers of the Judaeo-Christian tradition with which he frequently implicitly or explicitly identified himself, Jesus and Moses. Freud saw himself in that line of succession, and we must understand that if we are to understand psychoanalysis.

WILLIAMS: There was also, if I remember it from David Bakan's fascinating book[1] the fact that Freud was given the family Bible at the age of 33. The Jewish mystical tradition says you may not have the keys to the mysteries before then, and indeed all his messianic pronouncements came after that age. Freud's techniques, too, came directly out of that tradition. He called dreams "the royal road to understanding". But the interpretation of dreams, as well as word association, both of meaning and sound, as well as slips of the tongue, all that kind of thing, were in Freud's own mystical tradition. He also came from a region which produced many cabalistic and Chassidic teachers. Bakan even showed how certain pages of the Zohar consistently parallel certain pages in Freud's work, if you allow for certain transpositions which actually obey rules of word substitution formulated by Freud.

WEBSTER: There are all kinds of profound and direct relations to the Jewish mystical tradition and you are right to point towards his being given the family Bible. The inscription on the front page of that Bible was terribly

1. Sigmund Freud and the Jewish Mystical Tradition by David Bakan. Van Nostrand Co. Inc. 1958

important. I can't remember word for word, but Freud's father was saying in effect, "You have been given a special relationship with God, you have been allowed to see into the secrets of the universe by God". But we have to recognise that he lived in a predominantly Christian culture and was acutely aware of this, and in many respects, perhaps unwittingly, accommodated his own thinking to that culture. In some ways he produced out of his Jewish experience another version of Christianity, as had happened centuries before. Tucked away in the notes at the back of my book is a long quotation from David McLelland.

Now, McLelland, a Harvard psychologist and also a Christian, was writing in the 1960s about psychoanalysis as a religion. He was from a radical puritan background of Quakers himself, and was very interested in Freud as a religious leader. In fact, he more or less explicitly entertains the possibility that Freud might actually have been a divinely appointed prophet who had been sent by God to regenerate the Judaeo-Christian tradition in a way that would carry its message to a new secular generation. He actually seems to believe that Freud might have been a prophet sent by the God he professes not to believe in. So McLelland is pointing to a continuity of form, which is certainly there.

WILLIAMS: I've always thought that, because the source of Freud's ideas was from a true mystical tradition, therein lay their overwhelming power. I remember when I was about 15 lying in bed one night, wondering if I could think a psychological thought which was not flavoured by Freud. When I tried, it was virtually impossible. The fact that I could have that idea at all, at that age, without ever having read Freud, and living as I did in a house with no books, is very telling.

WEBSTER: That's absolutely fascinating. What you say conveys extremely well what Freud has become. Freud didn't have the creative influence on the culture he appears to have done. But he created an image of himself so powerful that we bestow on him everybody else's discoveries. We think that 'projection', for example, is something psychoanalysis discovered. But in the first place the word 'projection' is actually used in about 1856 by George Eliot, in her translation of Feuerbach, in a sense very similar to the way it is used in psychoanalysis. Shakespeare, too, clearly understood the process we label 'projection' very well indeed. That passage in *King Lear:*

Thou rascal beadle, hold thy bloody hand!
Why dost thou lash that whore? Strip thy own back;
Thou hotly lusts to use her in that kind
For which thou whip'st her.

So, profound and deep psychological insights were a part of our culture already. What is interesting about Freud is the sheer grandeur of the way he managed to persuade us that, before he came along, we didn't know any of these things. And what has happened now is that psychoanalysis has become a kind of dead-letter box. If there is an unidentified psychological insight going around which seems profound and deep, we say 'O that's Freudian'. It's curious. We enlarge his reputation and diminish our own at the same time. One of my concerns is that we too readily underestimate the wealth of our own ordinary psychological insights ...

WILLIAMS: Hear hear!

WEBSTER: ... and by disowning them, we then have to attribute them to somebody else. We attribute to Freud riches which are actually ours. We should repossess them. But critically and sceptically, because of course we too can be mistaken.

WILLIAMS: That young teenager who was me in the late 1950s, was literally possessed by 'Freudian' thoughts. But today I can think around the edges of Freudian ideas perfectly easily, because time has moved on. What was useful was digested by our culture and has become common knowledge, leaving bone and gristle, so to speak, to be chewed over by the faithful.

WEBSTER: But tell me what exactly these insights were that you refer to?
WILLIAMS: Those commonly assumed to originate in Freud's work. But now I'm uncertain, once you suggest that Freud's work is more like fly paper on which ideas - such as projection - which didn't have a context and category before, stick.
WEBSTER: I think Freud reinvented profound and complex insights like projection, like unconscious motivation - in a form which actually *emptied* them of their complexity and depth. In my opinion he was only able to reintroduce these ideas after he had first impoverished and pinned them into his own mechanistic system, where they became not part of a psychology of human nature but of a theory of medical therapeutics.
WILLIAMS: Can you give me an example?
WEBSTER: Take the idea of the unconscious. I would suggest that, instead of rediscovering that dark, resonant part of the human imagination which was already familiar to artists and poets, Freud took the cultural resonances of that idea and made them into medical concepts. He was primarily interested in the unconscious because he saw it as something which generated illness, and only secondarily interested in its relationship to the human condition. Because he insisted on understanding it in medical terms and then trying to use his medical understanding to illuminate human behaviour, he failed. His medical understanding was the very point where he entered his labyrinth of error.
WILLIAMS: He hijacked and warped ideas which had a place in the wider culture, in fact. I see that. And in order to do so, it was necessary for him to make the misrepresentations, which have latterly come to light. The cures which never happened; the wrong diagnoses, which did his patients a great deal of harm. He was virtually brainwashing them to see things his way and from this distance we can see that 'his way' helped Freud far more than it ever helped any patient.

WEBSTER: Yes. Freud not only does not have the extraordinary psychological insights we so frequently attribute to him, but on many occasions he shows himself almost devoid of ordinary psychological understanding. People now frequently talk about Freud in relation to the seduction theory, in relation to child sexual abuse, and they assume that Freud was deeply interested in the emotional consequences of that particular distortion of human relations. But if we go back to what Freud actually wrote, we discover Freud was scarcely interested in that at all. What interested him was what he saw as a kind of mechanical malfunction, caused by a series of instincts and drives whose operations were disturbed in a mechanical way. This is a profoundly reductionist aspect of Freud, and actually dangerous.
WILLIAMS: In what way?
WEBSTER: While I have some sympathy for the view of psychoanalysis as a means of restoring a vision of human nature to its necessary depth and complexity, providing us with that alternative to mechanical, reductionist approaches of biological psychiatry, I also think it is profoundly mistaken, and even dangerous. We do need to defend ourselves against the reductionist sterility of many aspects of our intellectual culture, but psychoanalysis is in itself one of the reductive ways of looking at human nature we should be trying to escape from! I am all for opposing biomedical models of mental illness. I think they are extremely damaging. But it is essential we should recognise that psychoanalysis was, in its origins, just such a model itself.

It is certainly true that people have tried to rescue Freud from his own intellectual origins. I have considerable sympathy for that enterprise. There are many interesting insights in some psychoanalytic adaptations of Freud's ideas. Freud's followers often had more profound insights than Freud himself. We failed to recognise that, and it needs to be recognised. But a good many of Freud's followers also went deeper into that labyrinth of error than Freud did.

Melanie Klein, in particular, has done great damage to English psychotherapeutic culture. Her method of interpreting children's play as though it was the voice of the unconscious, a kind of continual sexual soliloquy, has been disastrous, especially in the field of child protection. The kind of reckless 'disclosure therapy' which was criticised in the Butler-Sloss report on Cleveland is one of the legacies of this approach, and it is profoundly dangerous to the children themselves. In this respect psychoanalysis has left us with problems whose depth and severity we are only just beginning to recognise.

WILLIAMS: You say in your book you found yourself not only writing about Freud, but also writing the first prehistory of the illusory memory controversy; that all the miseries of 'recovered memories' trace straight back to Freud.

WEBSTER: Yes. Freud's seduction theory is in one respect the foundation stone of the recovered memory movement. As you know, Freud persuaded his daughter Anna, during her analysis, to accept that he had accurately reconstructed fantasies that she could not remember. Some people who read drafts of my book several years ago said this was an example of 'false memory'. False memory was less spoken about than now, and gradually it began to dawn on me, and others noted too, that the early history of psychoanalysis is where the recovered memory movement in the United States comes from. The foundation of the recovered memory movement is basically the version of psychoanalysis and its history which Freud himself constructed.

That version essentially claims that some of Freud's earliest patients, who had not been believed in the past, came to him with memories of sexual abuse which they wished to communicate, and that Freud gave them permission to speak, listened and understood. That of course is the version of Freud which has been put forward most influentially and powerfully by Jeffrey Masson in *The Assault on Truth.* Judith Herman put it forward even before Masson did, in *Father-*

Daughter Incest. And if we take it back even further, in 1979 or perhaps before, Florence Rush, an American social worker in a feminist conference, took the same view. But some more recent scholars of Freud have said this version of psychoanalysis is fundamentally false, and I agree. You could say it was one of Freud's own false memories - it seems he persuaded himself this is what had happened.

There was no question of women coming to Freud in 1896 and spontaneously telling him their memories of sexual abuse, and him listening and understanding. Freud himself said, 'Before they come for analysis the patients know nothing of these scenes." Nor was he interested in memories people could recall. His crucial belief was that if you could remember a traumatic event, in this case, sexual abuse, then it was not traumatic, not pathogenic. There is no suggestion anybody came to him with memories of sexual abuse. It was Freud, caught up in the conviction that he had discovered the 'source of the Nile' in terms of psychopathology, who decided that repressed memories of sexual abuse caused hysteria. And it was Freud who deliberately dug into his patients' unconscious, physically as well, by putting his hands on the patient's forehead and applying pressure, as if to squeeze out the supposed memories. This was the 'pressure method', and he would complain how exhausting it was.

WILLIAMS: This is medieval! Witchfinder stuff! No wonder they came up with the goods!

WEBSTER: When people said they had no such memories, Freud originated the doctrine of denial which now plays such a powerful role in our contemporary culture of child protection. The denial was in itself a sign of repression, a sign that these memories were actually there! Freud finally abandoned this seduction theory in 1897. But in *The Assault on Truth,* in 1984, Jeffrey Masson suggested that we must go back to that theory, which Freud originally expounded, and see that as the true, revolutionary tradition of psychoanalysis. Freud scholars all wonder why Freud abandoned the seduction theory. Masson, of course, says he had discovered the repressed secret of middle class Viennese society, but it was so troubling, and gave him so many problems with colleagues who saw him as a pornographer, that he abandoned it.

There is no evidence that this is what happened. There are other possibilities. Some people even take a very sanguine view and say Freud realised he was wrong. Well, that *would* be unusual!

Freud had some degree of insight into his methods, but not to the extent that he would abandon them because they didn't correspond with the real world. That wasn't his way. I think Freud abandoned the seduction theory because it was not viable. If your therapy consisted in uncovering crimes which had not been committed, it brought you into immediate conflict with the people you were indirectly accusing. This actually happened. One of Freud's patients told her father what Freud had said about her problem with sucking, and the father had the reaction of any parent falsely accused of sexual abuse by a therapist who has effectively created a false memory, or false construction of the woman's past. There was a furious row between Freud and the father.

I think what then happened was that Freud realised he needed to keep safe what he saw as his precious theory of repression from the refutation and anger of the world. So he decided he would preserve the theory of repression, which had led to the seduction theory, but would recover memories, not of crimes which had allegedly happened, which would inevitably lead to dispute and anger, but of uncontroversial or unwitnessed events, which were intrinsically uncheckable. Freud, in other words, retreated from a theory about what had happened in the real world, into a theory based on what happened inside the unconscious or, sometimes, on primal scenes such as parents having intercourse. These would be essentially unwitnessed.

WILLIAMS: Even in his own case, he himself said his memory of witnessing his mother naked was an assumption.

WEBSTER: Yes, indeed. But we should recognise that, by the time Masson's book was published in 1984, the psychotherapeutic tradition which had in many respects emerged out of psychoanalysis had become so emboldened, so confident, and so reinforced by various powerful ideologies, that it began once again to make rash pronouncements. The theory of repression could be used in a sort of quasi-psychoanalytic technique to recover real memories of controversial events - indeed of the child sexual abuse which Freud had originally interested himself in. Almost immediately it precipitated, in a massive way, the same kind of response that Freud had had from the parents of his patients! One can be pretty sure that, if Freud had not abandoned the seduction theory in 1897, there would very soon have been a false memory society in Vienna!

Another interesting inference can be drawn from all this. Freud was, as it were, in flight from the possibility of falsification, and therefore never tested out his theory of repression properly against real events. When the issue came up again in the 1980s, certain therapists were saying in effect: 'we are going to test out Freud's theory of repression, and test out the whole possibility of recovering repressed memories'. And, in the view of many, that testing has been disastrous. Very revealing, because it has shown how dangerous and ill-founded the original theory was.

But we must also remember where the theory of repression first came from. People do suffer traumas, they always have, and then they *do* forget events. There is a case of Charcot's, which I discuss in my book, where a man was wheeling a barrow along a road when he was run over by a passing carriage, hit his head, fell completely unconscious - and couldn't remember anything. But, because there was no visible injury, Charcot believed that his amnesia was caused by the traumatic nature of the accident. He did not recognise, as indeed few of his contemporaries would have done, that the man had suffered concussion from closed head injury or some such thing. In other words, the amnesia which had made the man forget the traumatic event was caused by injury to the brain.

And, improbable though it may seem to our psychotherapeutic culture, this is actually one of the main origins of Freud's entire theory of repression: a failure to recognise some of the more subtle forms of cerebral pathology.

WILLIAMS: That's an interesting demonstration of belief as a substitute for knowledge. But, on the subject of sexual 'memories', I am compelled to say what anyone with a shred of common sense can see - that Freud the great genius, for all his mighty influence, was also Freud the pervert, and his theories gave permission for all sorts of controlling, voyeuristic behaviour. When Dora is fidgeting during the analytic session, Freud says something like: "Ha! I know what that fidgeting is, you want to be scratching your genitals". And when psychoanalysing his own daughter, he speaks in explicit sexual detail in order to get specific sexual 'memories' out of her. In fact, he is putting explicit sexual ideas *into* his patients' minds, his own daughter included. Under the cloak of medical probity, he's just talking dirty!

WEBSTER: This is one of the most difficult aspects of Freud to discuss. He had virtually no insight into the deeply sexual nature of his interest in some of his patients, his own daughter included. He constructed some kind of explanation, but generally he was simply unaware of how he used his own theories to fantasise sexually about his patients. Behind that lack of awareness lay Freud's general lack of awareness of the entire realm of sexual fantasy. He did not appear to understand that sexual fantasies are an ordinary part of human consciousness, and seems to have thought they could only take place at an unconscious level. The fact that people knowingly fantasise without advertising the fact seems not to have occurred to him. Nor, obviously, that he was doing exactly the same kind of thing through his own theories.

WILLIAMS: I once saw that kind of cloaked lasciviousness in a Carmelite monk pretending to be concerned with a pretty young prostitute's welfare. There's none so blind as some who claim the moral authority to see more profoundly than the rest of us!

WEBSTER: Yes. When people accused Freud of engaging in pornographic conversations with his patients, which of course they did, he immediately accused them, quite aggressively, of not understanding medical objectivity. He managed to persuade himself almost completely that his interest in sexual matters was purely medical, purely that of the objective therapeutic doctor, and that he had risen beyond the kind of straightforward sexual interest which other people attributed to him.

WILLIAMS: Can we come now to your view of transference, because your view of this much discussed phenomenon in your book was the sanest and most plausible I have seen on this subject.

WEBSTER: Some people say transference is the key to all the mysteries, and that if you don't understand that you don't understand psychoanalysis. Now, if by transference we mean that people tend to play out with some adults they meet, patterns of relationship which have been established in their childhood in relation to their parents, I think that that is an ordinary and obvious observation of human nature, and I would not quarrel with it. But it is certainly not something which Freud could be credited with discovering. There is perhaps a tiny nucleus of truth in the idea of transference. But, as with many of Freud's concepts, he has elaborated around it a very specific and rigid structure which completely obscures, indeed in some respects destroys, any original truth the concept had.

The way I get to my view of transference is by observation. According to Freud's own theory at least, the psychoanalyst is impassive and objective and silent, and plays no part in the relationship. The patient is, as it were, reflected back from an impassive mirror.

Freud says it came as a great surprise when patients started to apparently fall in love with their psychoanalyst! Freud actually uses this term, 'appear to fall in love'. Again Freud is showing his extraordinary lack of psychological insight into human relationships.

He failed to see that the very theories of psychoanalysis have shaped the relationship and brought about this falling in love. Think of it. The patient is encouraged to reveal some of the most intimate secrets of his or her soul, some of the most embarrassing aspects of their memories and their past, in a way which is actually only primarily done in relationships of love and trust. It may sometimes be an invitation to intimacy, in that someone revealing their deepest secrets is doing so as a gesture of trust, as an invitation to the other person to reciprocate, an invitation to love.

Again, what Freud does not understand is how vulnerable people are when they reveal these intimate secrets, and the terrible feelings of insecurity which doing so engenders. We habitually keep these kind of things to ourselves because we know our vulnerability, and that we may be opening ourselves to the possibility of rejection. When people confess these intimate secrets, whether in the traditional Roman Catholic or psychotherapeutic sense, they need reassurance that what they have revealed does not, after all, render them unlovable.

I think that is part of what Freud was observing. Patients wanting therapists to love them still, even though they have revealed deep secrets. And the psychoanalysts impassively refusing to do so. There would be great dangers if the psychoanalyst did plunge into the relationships they construct, (and that often happens), but for orthodox psychoanalysts the prescription was that the analyst should remain distant, remote, in some sort of heaven of objectivity, far above, as it were, the vulnerable patient squirming on the couch. And it doesn't take much imagination to realise that we are here constructing something very similar to the relationship of the poor unclean sinner confessing his uncleanness and sinfulness before God, and being thereby driven into a relationship of worship and adulation for this heavenly father whose love is now psychologically indispensable.

What I am suggesting is that Freud has recreated the profound psychological dynamics of the confessional in all kinds of complex ways, which generally speaking we do not recognise. Freud himself accepted that there was some kind of parallel between psychoanalysis and the confessional, but we have tended to leave that at a superficial level. It is only if we start to try and really understand in some deep and complex way the psychodynamics of the traditional confessional that we see how interesting and illuminating the parallel is.

WILLIAMS: And here is your underlying theme. Once you have presented and inspected the evidence and analysed your material, alarming us along the way with the emotional brutalising many patients underwent, we come to the fulcrum, the hinge of the book. Freud's theory of human behaviour, which appears to scientise life, the universe, and everything in it, seems to eliminate God completely. But, in fact, it leaves God omnipresent, lurking in the machine.

WEBSTER: Yes. Although Freud himself would see psychoanalysis as a way of freeing ourselves from the superstitious residues of ordinary theism, of religion, or whatever you call it, I think he recreated religion in secular form. There is an important point here which critics, who are themselves committed to rationalism, tend to miss: one of the things we don't recognise generally, one of the reasons we don't understand Freud's kind of rationalism, is that Judaeo-Christian monotheism itself has always been intolerant of other people's religious faith.

Unless we understand that the desire of rationalism to eliminate God, or to expunge religion, is actually part of our Judaeo-Christian heritage, part of our intolerance of superstitious faith, we don't understand the engine and the dynamic of rationalism. That engine and dynamic comes from religion - because our Judaeo-Christian tradition is a rationalist tradition. It has always been deeply opposed to ritualistic or superstitious forms of faith. Rationalism, as Freud himself espoused it, is simply the Judaeo-Christian sensibility in disguise, intolerant of ritualistic and superstitious faiths.

What we need is not to expunge religion but to explain it. Freud's was an attempt to expunge and eradicate, and very dangerous because expunging and eradicating the religious faith of others is a form of crusading. And we know how dangerous crusading can be.

WILLIAMS: It seems to me he made a massive attempt to control the world, as primitive people do. Whenever I read Freud's work, or read about it, I see this attempt to control and impose order both as a novelist does, who says 'come, see the world my way', (and I'm not the first to point out what a magnificent novelist Freud would have been), but also in an attempt to control in a more fundamentalist religious way. Do you agree?

WEBSTER: Yes. I think that Freud, in his role as a leader, in his desire to control his own followers, found it essential to *prescribe* certain doctrines and to *proscribe* others he thought were undermining the central truths of psychoanalysis.

WILLIAMS: And those who questioned the dogma were viciously excommunicated.

WEBSTER: I think that's terribly important to note. He demonised people. He actually said in a letter about one of his critics that he came in and filled up the room with his 'devil's stench'. That is not just a slip of the pen. It profoundly encapsulates Freud's attitude to those who disagreed with him. He was vicious, he demonised them, sometime overtly, sometimes by employing psychoanalytic terminology, which is a slightly more polite way of being rude to people.

WILLIAMS: Yes, I found almost incredible the psychoanalytic description you quote of Jonathan Swift, But I'd like to ask your opinion on this; were there any valid cures, any chance that, in going to a Freudian analyst, you would get more than the predictable percentage of cure it has been well established is gained by talking to anyone in a therapeutic setting, even someone untrained? Do you think the specifics of psychoanalysis itself, over and above the ordinary human contact, ever genuinely helped anybody?

WEBSTER: I would want to say it almost certainly has. The central criticisms in my book are not levelled against psychoanalysis, which contains many schools and many approaches, and which is enriched, in some cases, by the ordinary psychological insights which psychoanalysts bring to psychoanalysis. My main criticisms are of Freud. Some psychoanalysts have had a much richer vision of human nature than Freud did, and not all psychoanalysts adhere to classical psychoanalysis and Freud's own doctrines. I think therapeutically helpful things can almost be smuggled in as contraband. If they are a help, then, of course people give the credit to Freud.

WILLIAMS: And Freud himself?

WEBSTER: In so far as any religious leader can bring to the people who become followers or disciples, feelings of comfort, reassurance, certainty, in that sense Freud was similar to many other religious leaders. He certainly gave people the kinds of feelings which religious people genuinely are grateful for. But, as a psychotherapist or a healer, which is how Freud I suppose would have perceived himself. No. I do not think that Freud conferred any benefits in that capacity at all.

WILLIAMS: Given what you and I know about cults, it seems to me that if the content of Freud's work had not been so medically based, his happy band of warriors could have ended up like those in Waco.

The signs are there... Expelling and demonising dissenters, involving himself voyeuristically with female 'disciples', you are wrong, he is always right, the 'pressure technique' to squeeze out the demons. It's only a matter of degree.

WEBSTER: I would say not. That view overlooks the essential orthodoxy of Freud's vision. He had no wish to lead a small dissenting cult on the fringes of society. He wished to be a prophet in the central tradition. It's one of the interesting paradoxes - how did a set of doctrines so apparently unsettling and unfamiliar, becomes so rapidly and widely accepted. I think the answer is, again, that at some deep level it was not unfamiliar and not unsettling.

It was deeply reassuring because it brought back, as I have said, the oldest and the most central doctrines of the Judaeo-Christian tradition. Freud wanted to be the ultimate insider, and needed the power of orthodoxy behind him.

WILLIAMS: We haven't mentioned the Oedipus complex, one of the cornerstones of the theory. As a lover of stories myself, I always found it very miserly of Freud to focus almost exclusively on one story out of the many available.

WEBSTER: I think the Oedipus complex was a genuine Freudian false memory. In his biography of Freud, Ernest Jones says something to the effect that, during the course of his psychoanalysis, Freud uncovered memories of a time when, travelling by train, he had seen his mother naked, and been aroused by this sight. Now, when one develops the scepticism about uncovering memories to unravel what actually happened, one is immediately doubtful about this account. Go back to what Freud wrote to Wilhelm Fliess in 1897 about the Oedipus complex, and you discover that it wasn't like that at all. Freud did not uncover or recover a memory of anything. At a certain point, when he was quite young, he went on a long train journey with his mother, a journey so long he *deduced* they must have slept on the train, and *deduced* that he then might have seen his mother undressing. It was from this reconstructed possibility that Freud conjured up the idea that perhaps he might once have seen his mother naked and been sexually aroused. Having artificially constructed what I call this false memory, he used it again and again.

This is characteristic of Freud's world-conquering confidence. An essentially shaky and ill-founded notion is used to conquer the whole field of psychopathology. Since he had this experience (which of course he hadn't), he decided everybody else must have had it as well, and therefore this was a fundamental aspect of childhood development.

But how did Freud come to this conclusion? Why was he writing to Fliess about it? Because Fliess had observed to Freud that he had seen his son have an erection, when considerably younger than Freud had been, and he too arrived at the did conclusion that this was in response to seeing his mother naked. That in itself is pure conjecture. But it seems to be how the Oedipus complex came about.

WILLIAMS: He chose the Oedipus story because it suited the warp of his own personality, I suppose. And then generalised his personal response to an imaginary event to make this behaviour structure inevitable at all times and under all circumstances for the whole human race! And many of us have believed it for more than a hundred years.

WEBSTER: We invest in the Oedipus complex our own understanding of deep, complex and ambivalent emotional relationships with our mothers, or other people with their mothers. And we say - this is the kind of thing Freud was talking about. And make the Oedipus complex into something much more interesting, with much greater psychological resonance, than it ever had for Freud himself. Again, as in other aspects of his thinking, Freud did not see the Oedipus complex as referring to the complex of emotional relationships between mother and son. He saw it very much as a stage in a mechanical process of development. Maybe Freud subsequently tried to fill his rather empty mechanical concept with more psychological riches, but it remained fundamentally a theory about biological development.

WILLIAMS: What about the respectable scientific notion of doing research?

WEBSTER: Freud would believe that he had in some way

tested this theory and found the evidence for it but then he only formulated theories of the kind which were, so to speak, self-confirming. Because of the very nature of the concept of the unconscious he could confirm any theoretical construct. The unconscious was a kind of bank on which Freud could endlessly draw theoretical cheques, as though there was a great wealth of evidence deposited there that would support any of his findings. The reality always was that there was nothing at all in the bank. The great tragedy for Freud was that he himself never realised this.

Robin Skynner on Life

***Ivan Tyrrell** finds out why **Robin Skynner** and **John Cleese** wrote the ultimate how-to book, 'Life and How To Survive It' ,and how the process changed them.*

IVAN TYRRELL: Your previous book with John Cleese, *Families and How To Survive Them,* was written for the general public but quickly became recommended reading for therapists and counsellors, almost a textbook. The same will undoubtedly happen to your new book, *Life and How To Survive It,* which I must say I've enjoyed reading. Is there anything you would like to address more specifically to therapists that you didn't put in the book?

ROBIN SKYNNER: Well, I'm a bit hesitant about talking to other professionals for reasons that centre around the fact that my own interest in therapy was a purely selfish one. It developed because I wanted to find out about myself and the world and make sense of things. But if want to know about something, and I feel I can be useful, I'm happy to speak up. I am also, however, quite happy for everyone to go off in their own direction.

When I began work in family therapy there was little written material we could use to help us. There was some work being done in America but it was difficult to get hold of in those days, so I began writing, and writing became an enormous pleasure to me. I gathered people around me, formed groups and bounced ideas off them. Then organisations evolved out of the work we were doing - like The Institute for Family Therapy. But all the time I was just following my own selfish interest - trying to satisfy my curiosity and wanting to find other people who would explore this with me. The reason I became a little more known was because I wrote about it and what I wrote was useful, in the same way that maps are useful for people following in your footsteps.

There are three things I've learnt over the years which may be of interest to other therapists. The first is to do with the relationship we all need to have with patients in order not to influence them unconsciously in the direction of our own beliefs. The received wisdom tends towards saying that, as therapists, we should be neutral and avoid bringing our own personal or family life into the therapy work. Having a more direct real relationship with patients is conventionally seen as harmful. But I found the reverse is true.

I now understand that, when you are more yourself in the therapy situation, when you give your own views and bring in your own family and relationships as examples, provided it's always done with an eye on being beneficial and serving the treatment process (and isn't just because you want to talk about yourself), it's very helpful.

When you give examples that are real to you, somehow you set patients free to have their own views.

Of course, it's quite right that at the beginning of your career as a therapist that you should keep a clear distinction between you and the patient. It's a good tightrope to walk when one is learning, but in the long run I think that the process of getting out of the way of the patient's development is to do with being more yourself.

The second thing, connected with that idea, is that the main benefit a patient gets from a therapist depends on the quality of the therapist as a person. Everything else is secondary to that. You may have enormous powers and techniques and theoretical knowledge but, in the end, what really matters is who you are. That's fundamental.

This doesn't mean that people who don't want to see things that way, who want to use, for example, a behavioural method, shouldn't do so. Not at all. That's absolutely fine because they are staying within their own limits. We should all stay within our limits. If a therapist wants to use a more structured approach - some technique which is laid out and can be systematically followed - it's fine. It's as if they are holding a lifeline because they can't trust themselves not to be swept overboard if they let go. If they hang on, they and their patients will be safe. All kinds of therapy can be useful and there is room for all sorts of people in it. But it benefits everybody if therapists know what their limitations are. If a therapist says "I don't want to look inside myself, I don't think I can face it". Fine. In fact, therapists who can't face themselves are often very good with patients who can't face themselves. That's the way it works out. I am increasingly impressed by the fact that somehow people tend to get the kind of therapists that suit them - although sometimes, of course, great mistakes are made.

The third thing is that one should enjoy oneself in this work. I am suspicious of therapists claiming altruistic motives. The money motive's fine, it's clean. And doing therapy to enjoy oneself because one likes using the skill, like a carpenter enjoying making something out of wood, that's clean too. But, where someone claims to do it to help other people, then it probably won't stand up to examination, although that's how we usually all start.

TYRRELL: Well, there is bound to be an element of self-deception in being a therapist. The fact that most of us are not weaned off the need for attention when we're young, and grow up not understanding the attention factor in situations, ensures that. We don't realise, for example, that the type of career we choose can be just a complex attention getting device. I'm sure that, for many therapists, the attention they get by taking on that role is a form of payment, though they may not recognise it as such.

SKYNNER: Yes, but I think it's still pretty safe, unless the therapist is malevolent or irresponsible. It is a natural basic thing to enjoy helping people. And this enjoyment doesn't necessarily come out of duty or some compulsive need to help other people, which is often doing something for other people that you should have done for yourself. But enjoyment is different - I enjoyed my work enormously. It's a great pleasure to see people getting better, but I'm clear in my mind that this is not the motive I started with. Then I was really helping other people because I didn't want to see how I could help myself.

TYRRELL: Are you saying that in helping yourself you automatically almost always help other people?

SKYNNER: Yes, it follows automatically. All good therapists therefore are mainly concerned with sorting themselves out. I remember, when I first realised this, telling groups on more than one occasion that to do good group therapy all I really needed to do was to learn to enjoy myself and turn up! Never mind anything else.

For over thirty years, I made it a practice to take a week off at half-term. I told the patients to continue without me. I just explained that I needed to take time off occasionally, so I would feel better and therefore be more useful to them, but it was bad for them to take time off because it would interrupt the therapeutic process. They often thought this was outrageous but they usually met and had a very productive session in the sense that they would say all the things they couldn't say while I was there. Particularly a lot of things about me... so I usually got 'what for' when I came back! They would gang up on me and challenge me and laugh a lot, and talk about sex and not tell me what they'd been talking about, and so on. They became free.

Now, although I certainly arranged this originally because I wanted to have more holidays, the result was that it speeded up the process because people became independent of me more quickly. The value of leaving a group on its own once in a while was a great lesson and something I discovered by chance.

Such discoveries fascinate me and at each stage of my life I found myself wanting to bring together a number of people who would explore these things with me. I was always exploring, it was like climbing a mountain to see further, but eventually, when I wanted to climb higher and explore social, political and spiritual areas, I ran out of people. Society, of course, needs settled ground. It needs to build an encampment on the mountainside. Climbers need a base and an encampment to return to, but most people are not climbers. Most are happy to climb just a little way and then stay in the comparative safety of an encampment. You need institutions in order to teach and so on, these are the encampments, but institutions fossilise and I've never been interested in staying in one place. I always wanted to go further on up the mountainside to something else. I can't explain why. My connection with John Cleese came about because of this. He was the only person I found who really was willing to go to the limit and see where it took him. And the books we've done together came out of that.

TYRRELL: Yes. When reading your latest book I was struck by the wide range of research material you have both absorbed and how that helps you understand yourselves and other people. The core theme of the book, for example, is based on little-known research into what constitutes a 'healthy' family. Now this enthusiasm for research findings contrasts with my impression that many psychologists, doctors and therapists - 'specialists' - seem to care little of what researchers outside their subject have found out about group behaviour and how the mind and body work. Isn't it odd that so many people have such a low level of interest in such research?

SKYNNER: Yes, people often settle for a lot less information than perhaps they should. The way John and I worked together on this is partly an attempt to overcome this tendency. We present the research findings in an easily digestible form.

TYRRELL: Was John Cleese the only one you found who could go further with you? Weren't there others?

SKYNNER: No, there weren't others. I really did run out of colleagues I could do this with.

TYRRELL: What characteristics do you think he has that made him do that?

SKYNNER: Well it's connected partly to the quality he has that underlies his ability as a comedy actor. He has a willingness to turn everything upside down, throw old ideas overboard or push them to extremes. He also has a brilliant and perceptive mind and a tremendous range of interests. We also share a similarity in that we both always want to test things out - to test things to breaking point. Don't ask me why... though I'd like to know.
TYRRELL: Perhaps it's something to do with that inner search. Something in you wants to understand about behaviour and groups and society and different cultures and so on. And, although any gathering of people that meet regularly will automatically form into a mini-cult, maybe there must be, in any population, some individuals who counteract that, otherwise humanity would fossilise completely. Did you notice cliques and cults forming in the organisations and groups you initiated?
SKYNNER: Well, it probably did happen in ways I didn't realise. It is inevitable. Moreover, I suspect I have my own belief system that I don't see and which people take on. But, in so far as I was aware of this process, I would always stand things on their head. If someone started agreeing with me too much, or having a fixed belief about something, I would dynamite it. I would put it in doubt, automatically.
TYRRELL: That, in itself, is an ancient way of teaching people about the nature of reality - that reality is not to be found in words and beliefs...
SKYNNER: Yes, that's right. To me what's healthy is being open to the world, which is changing all the time. And if one is properly in contact with the changing nature of everything - always open to new experience one is constantly changing oneself. Unfortunately, however, we all have a tendency to attach ourselves, and hang on to, security blankets or teddy bears or whatever. Ideas, conventional behaviour, groups and cults are all security blankets that people cling to. But mature adults don't need security blankets, so that's something I

always try to shake people free from. And myself, of course.
TYRRELL: Yes, security is fundamental to a helpless baby. We need a security blanket when we first come into the world. But as we grow up we should come to tolerate more uncertainty - after all, no-one in the world can absolutely guarantee that we will be alive tomorrow. When, however, an obsession with security continues into adult life it prevents us developing a sense of reality.
SKYNNER: And it's not an either/or thing either - either being open to experience and throwing everything overboard or clinging to some certainty. We are always moving between these two states. We would go mad if we lost all security or certainty. On the other hand we become ossified, rigid and fixated if we cling on too much. So it is always a matter of oscillating between the two. And, in therapeutic work, finding that balance is crucially important. To start with one has to hold people's hands quite tightly to help them feel secure, then, gradually, you free them.

I've noticed a lot of therapies emphasise one approach or the other - either to have some belief system or have no belief system. But I believe we have to start from some point in between.
TYRRELL: When I watch skilled hypnotherapists at work I am struck by the fact that the lighter and more open-ended the technique they employ, say with metaphors, the more automatically they seem to stimulate a healing process in the brain of their patients, who then start to heal themselves. The results are often spectacular and it occurred to me that similar things might happen in family group therapy. Do you ever introduce open-ended ideas or concepts into the situation for the person or group to develop themselves?
SKYNNER: Yes. There is a pervading set of ideas in family therapy now called 'constructivism' which says that people organise the world in a certain way and if you present any other story to them, this will enable them to change and solve their problem. It's true up to a point because people

get locked into a particular view, a particular explanational story, about what they are like and why they have difficulties and so on. If one just offers them a different view of it, even if it's not right - in fact it certainly won't be absolutely right! - they can't help but challenge their own story. But I think that what's missing in the theories about this is that, just by giving an alternative view to patients, you immediately change the perception they've been attached to. I am amazed at the number of times people simply hadn't thought of doing something different. So, if you present them with a different story, one that you just made up - even a really crazy one - what makes the difference is not your story but the fact that you revealed that other patterns of resources are available to them. It's like the Japanese. They were isolated from the rest of the world for over a thousand years. They had nothing to compare their system with, whereas we in the West had experience of other countries, kingdoms and governments, all of which operated in different ways to our own. But, because the Japanese didn't have that, they couldn't be anything other than rigid conformists. They found it difficult to think of something different because they had no idea something different was possible. Once you see this it explains so much about the Japanese people and their relationship with the rest of the world.

It's a bit like when you have a one-parent family and the parent wants to set the children free but the children end up with no idea of what a different form of parenting would be like. With two-parent families you've always got someone arguing and disagreeing, at least some of the time - two parents are never going to agree completely on everything - so children are brought up with a model of difference right from the beginning of their lives and can learn that nothing is absolutely true. But this is much harder for children of a one-parent family to see.

The sickening thing about all these fundamental things which we are so slow to change in ourselves, is that we're slow because we don't know we can change.

TYRRELL: Yes. It's as if we're living out our life on one shelf, vaguely aware there are other shelves below us, because we can look down, but quite unable to conceive of other shelves up above where life could be quite different.
SKYNNER: That's right. When you're ignorant of history, it just repeats itself. I've found that life is the best teacher and that brings me to another point about therapists.

The majority of psychotherapists tend, if in doubt, to recommend that people have therapy. They see therapy as only a good thing and tend to feel that everyone can benefit from it. This is not a view I share.

When someone comes to see me I say to myself, "Can we avoid therapy here?" I tend to push people away, not because I don't think it's valuable for people who really want it, but because I think it works much better when they really do want it. I believe, much more than most therapists, in the healing processes of life. I prefer it that way. It's more real and avoids all the problems of giving up a huge amount of your time and independence, going back to the womb and so on. So, although I'm obviously in favour of therapy in the sense that I have practised it all my life and enjoyed it and I think it's effective, I first push people away from it. But if they then push me back and say, "Well, yes, but we want it anyway" it is more likely to do them good then. Because of this I suppose I've done more work than most therapists have only seeing patients infrequently; once a month, or every three months, or even annually.

There was a couple who came to see me about every three years to discuss whether they should have therapy or not. They always asked for it, but didn't take it up. After they had done this about three times and ten years had gone by, the next time I saw them I was quicker off the mark. When they said, 'Can we have some therapy?' I said, 'Well, I don't think you are ready for it yet. What I would like you to do, if you can get your diary out, is make a note here that you'll come to see me again in three years time to discuss the idea of

having therapy. I think you should go on doing this for the rest of your life. Within a few weeks they began!
TYRRELL: What do you think prevents so many of us from learning about ourselves?
SKYNNER: Well, it seems to me that the belief that one should try to control and change the world to help other people is a major cause of that. It is easy to be misdirected. Politicians, for example, try to change the world and other people. By chance they are sometimes useful to society but, because they are focusing all their attention outside, trying to shift the world around them rather than changing themselves, they are poor learners. Consequently they tend to do more harm than good.

It's the same with many therapists, I'm sure. There is a similar dynamic at work if they are more concerned with helping others rather than helping themselves. But this is only one of the possible reasons. Some people are just too rigid and terrified to learn - afraid of change. They hang grimly on to some relationship, belief system, group or cult and sort of nail themselves to that.

I've often thought that my desire to know more was motivated by greed. Not that I feel that greed is always such a bad thing. When patients first come to therapy and we form a new group, it is usually motivated to start with by envy. They all sit there waiting for someone else to speak first. No one gives anything so no one takes anything. Nothing happens. Then there is certain point in the development of a group when envy gives way to greed. And that's marvellous! I want to fly a flag up over the building when that happens. Everyone starts grabbing, taking, arguing, shouting and, of course, in the process, putting things in.
TYRRELL: Like trading. You have to put something in to get something out?
SKYNNER: Yes. Even if you just talk about yourself, you're putting something in which then activates other people to put things in and the whole thing begins. We can't avoid greed.

It's built into our genes and can be constructive up to a point. In that sense I see greed as more positive, or at least leading to more interesting possibilities.

But fear is a different matter. Fear and envy paralyses everything and can bring about destruction.

TYRRELL: Perhaps this is connected to the mood in Europe and America at the moment. There is a lot of talk now about values, violence and crime in society. It's even suggested that a Royal Commission be set up to look at the morals of the country! What do you think about that kind of thing.

SKYNNER: Well, I've read lots of articles on this violence issue recently and they mainly point out that, although things are a bit different at the moment, exactly the same kind of violence happened in the 50s with teddy boys beating up people with chains. The violence was just the same for the victims and the perpetrators. But I think there is a change now and that is that there is a lesser sense of responsibility within society about it.

I can't see a Royal Commission producing anything positive. Although it's probably good for people to talk about it. A Royal Commission would only lead to people saying "Oh, we can wait until the report comes out". The trouble is, it is years until they report. And in the meantime nothing happens. It's very like therapy. An enormous amount of couple therapy stops the problem being solved. People come along when they are just coming to a crisis in their lives, perhaps just about to separate or bring about some major change, and the therapist says, "Oh, well, let's see if we can do something about this, there might be some hope, there may be something we can do. I'll book in six appointments for you. " And of course, everyone waits and nothing changes until another six months has gone by. Which is why, when working with couples, I often only see them once to help them clarify the effect on their life of an absolute crisis. At the point of making a decision, only they can make it. No one else can do it for them. They have to do it for themselves.

But somehow helping them face the truth, and presenting it in a clear way to them, at the right time, is vital. If you offer therapy in a naive way however, you can stop people reaching a necessary crisis.

In family therapy we deliberately generate a crisis sometimes - actually arrange it - because we want to bring things to a point where there is enough force to move the clients into another constellation. I often take an egg box, one of those where you can put a little ping-pong ball in, and show people how, if you try to push the ping-pong ball up the slope, it falls back, and, in order to change the position of the ping-pong ball, you have to give the box a bang. It's like that.

TYRRELL: I wonder if there is a parallel between bringing troubled couples and families to a crisis and how society changes?

SKYNNER: Well, that's a good question. I think there probably is. Things only change when they get bad enough. I've always been interested in parallels between therapy and society because, as I said, I like to explore new areas. I was able to do this in the book with John because it interests him too.

TYRRELL: In the chapter on spirituality in *Life...* you used the Sufi teaching story, *The Blind Men and the Elephant,* to illustrate how difficult it is to show people a larger pattern that you can see but they cannot and how they cannot help but accuse you of being unscientific if you talk about a larger picture that they are 'connected' to but cannot grasp. This is a difficult area. Are there people in your life you can talk to about this?

SKYNNER: If people have similar experiences to you, you can talk to them. If they haven't, you can't. It's like when you have a baby. It means nothing until you've had one yourself, then you don't stop talking about it. You are suddenly one of the club.

TYRRELL: Do you see in society then a sort of hierarchy of understanding, as if it's almost a function of humanity to

'grow' people to become connected to the universe in the way you describe in your book - that would mean that the rest of us are like the millions of acorns that never grow into oak trees - or do you think that human evolution is a chance thing and has no meaning?
SKYNNER: Oh, I think probably the first. However, I don't know, but it makes a kind of sense to me that there is a design. It just doesn't seem likely that there is no pattern to everything at a deeper level. But that chapter on spirituality is the one which I am most unhappy about because I don't know. John and I often disagree over it. He tries to follow it logically. For example, he would say that the more healthy people are, the more likely they will be to have this sort of mystical experience. And I don't know that that's true at all.
TYRRELL: Yes, I can see why. In the book, when you discuss the findings about the healthy family experiments, you said there was a tendency for 'healthy' people to have a sense of 'spiritual connection' to something greater than themselves. Churches, however, by their very nature, tend not to be interested in 'seekers after truth'. It is against their interest for people to try and free themselves. They offer comfort and security, of course, but their main concern is to bind you to a package of beliefs and behaviour. This is the opposite of searching for meaning and connectedness beyond the confines of a belief system. That's why, after all, religious people confidently proclaim they have all the answers and that we need look no further. Not so long ago the Church attacked and burnt people who sought truth from outside.
SKYNNER: That's true. And it still goes on.
TYRRELL: So, if these findings about the churchgoing healthy people you described are true, they might not be interested in searching in the sense you describe?
SKYNNER: That's possible, perhaps because they are not troubled enough.
TYRRELL: People have pointed out that it is the Christians who are asking for a Royal Commission on morals in society,

and encouraging us all to be concerned and so on, are really admitting their own failure. After all, they've had nearly 2,000 years to get it right but, because they trapped themselves inside a belief system, they seem so often now to know less than ordinary people. It's rather odd to me that, when priests and bishops lay claim to a higher moral ground, people still give them credit for knowing what they're talking about. Christian leaders, in their strange costumes, seem like slow motion Pied Pipers of Hamelin who have lost their magic but are still attempting to lead people off somewhere far away from anything real. Not 'spiritual' at all, just emotional.
SKYNNER: I agree. There is a vacuum. That's why I felt we had to have a go in that area. When you look at the fundamentalists who want to kill Salman Rushdie or the Catholic/Protestant divide in Northern Ireland, that's not religion. Or rather, it's religion on a low level of psychological health, as we show in the book. As you come up the levels of health the whole relationship changes in a way that makes sense and it explains some of the puzzles about, for example, how Christianity created the Inquisition. The Inquisition is a natural consequence when religion is controlled by unhealthy people. Once you see that, there is no contradiction.
TYRRELL: What did you and John Cleese learn from this project?
SKYNNER: This is something we didn't talk about in the book. I wish we had now. We started the process by brain-storming. We sat around the table or went for walks with the tape recorder and just free-associated about it all. John has this incredible capacity to turn absolutely everything upside down. He just pillaged and destroyed the knowledge I had spent decades learning. He kept coming at what I thought I knew from totally new angles - this zany lateral thinking of his. He forced me to re-jig all my thoughts and look at everything afresh from underneath rather than on top. We also tried to boil every idea and word down. He was insistent

that what we said should be in simple language, so that everyone could understand it. No jargon. This turned out to be important. We found that, because we were trying to express everything in simple language, we had to take everything to breaking point to sort it out. We reached down to a deeper level of simplicity, to the foundations where everything began to follow from simple principles. This meant that, although we started out trying to write an outline of existing knowledge, we actually ended up with an integration of existing knowledge - something which has never been achieved in this field before, and can't be achieved at an academic level because there is not enough agreement.

The other interesting thing we did was that, in order to understand more, we examined ourselves for any signs of any particular behaviour we happened to be looking at. For example, we would talk about schizophrenia and autism and I started to discover that I had elements of schizophrenic and autistic behaviour in myself. We really lived the book. I went through periods when I felt quite schizophrenic and quite autistic and came to realise that these states were part of me and, somehow, health has something to do with integrating all those elements at different levels and having access to them. John didn't have that experience exactly, but he does remember getting bogged down and writing terribly slowly in the section on depression and then racing through at top speed when we were working on mania! We worked on these two books for thirteen years and both of us changed enormously as a consequence. It was a continuous process of editing and refinement. There were six or seven drafts.

TYRRELL: Yet it still flows like a conversation.

SKYNNER: Well, that's the idea. The art of writing is to conceal the effort. We hope we've concealed it so well that readers don't notice there's any art there at all. By working in this way, we thought it might have an effect on people - actually get inside them - so that, if they resisted with their intellects, it could soak in through the skin. That's why we used so much humour, which we couldn't avoid anyway with John. Also, writing it in the form of conversation gave me the chance to employ all kinds of therapeutic techniques that I'd been using in therapy sessions.

One example not in the book comes from when my wife Prue and I used to work together with couples. If we got stuck with a particularly resistant family we would ask their permission if she and I could have a word with each other, explaining that "we felt we weren't doing a good enough job and had got a bit stuck somewhere". And then we'd say, "well, it will save time, if you don't mind, if we don't leave the room and we just stay here and talk about you, just don't take any notice, don't listen to us if you don't mind". Then we would talk away to each other in front of the family, as if they weren't there, and whatever we said then went straight in without any resistance at all. We worked together so well. So, while writing the book, John would put himself on the line saying he had this problem, when really he was talking about something that other people have difficulty with.

When we were last speaking to the staff at Tavistock I could see that one of the therapists there was sort of creeping around to ask a question about whether, in writing this book, we were doing a 'wrong' thing and she asked John, "Do you think that, possibly, in writing this book you were trying to get some more therapy?" And he said, "Well, yes! Of course!"

The blind ones and the matter of the elephant

THERE WAS once a city where all the inhabitants were blind. One day a king with his entourage and army arrived and camped outside the city walls. He had with him a mighty elephant which he used in attack on his enemies and to increase the people's awe wherever he went.

On hearing about this creature, the blind populace became anxious for information about it. Some of the sightless ones made their way to the king's camp and were allowed into the presence of the mighty beast. But since they did not even know the form or shape of the elephant, they could only grope sightlessly, gathering information by touching some part of it.

Then, each thinking he knew something, they returned to their fellow citizens inside the city. Eager groups clustered around them, misguidedly anxious to learn the truth from those who were themselves astray.

They asked about the form and shape of the elephant, and listened to all that they were told. When the man whose hand had reached an ear told about the elephant's nature he said, "it is a large, rough thing, wide and broad, like a carpet"

The one who had felt the trunk said, "I have the real facts about it, it is like a straight and hollow pipe, awful and destructive."

The one who had felt its legs said, "No! It is mighty and firm, like a pillar.' Each had felt one part out of many. Each had perceived it wrongly. No mind knew all. Knowledge is not the companion of the blind. All had imagined something, but something incorrect. The created is not informed about divinity. There is no Way in this science by means of the ordinary intellect.

The above is the 13th century teaching story by Mualana Jalaluddin Rumi referred to by Robin Skynner in Life and How To Survive It.

Ritual - a healing journey

*Theatre director and writer, **James Roose-Evans** is also a priest. **Barry Winbolt** spoke to him about his innovative work helping therapists with ritual.*

BARRY WINBOLT: Ritual is a term which many people associate with customs in other cultures, yet it is shown to fulfil an important function in our lives and social well-being. What do you see as ritual, and what is its function?
JAMES ROOSE-EVANS: Ritual takes many forms. At the simplest level there are those recurring personal rituals which we all use: for getting up in the morning, going off to work, coming home, relaxing, going to bed. All such personal rituals enable us to come to terms with the reality of each day, imposing some kind of order on what otherwise might be chaos. There are rituals relating to every aspect of life: rituals of dress, which is to do with our identity and the way in which we do or do not reveal ourselves to others; of courting; of sexuality; of the office or work-place. Then there are the more complex rituals evolved for the family, clan, tribe or nation. These more classic rituals all place the individual in a larger context, so that birth, puberty, marriage and death are seen as timeless experiences which have occurred to generations of individuals. Such rituals serve to validate and reinforce our ability to cope with an unpredictable world. They heighten the intensity of shared experience so we realise that we are not alone, but part of an indivisible whole.
WINBOLT: Originally, I understand, you first began to explore ritual when you were working with actors. Can you explain briefly how you came to be doing the work with ritual that you are today?
ROOSE-EVANS: I first began, in the mid-'50s, while teaching in New York at the Julliard School of Music. I was looking at the theatre as ritual and ritual as theatre. Since then, I have continued to explore ritual and the need for ritual in society

today in my workshops. I have worked with professional actors and performers all around the world, and in recent years I have been asked to work with therapists and psychoanalysts.

WINBOLT: Do you ever work exclusively with groups of therapists?

ROOSE-EVANS: Not exclusively; an average group at a workshop is likely to include some professional performers, a couple of people from other walks of life and a growing number of therapists.

WINBOLT: You draw then on your work in theatre, and, in 1981, were ordained as a non-stipendiary priest in the Anglican Church, which must be a major influence.

ROOSE-EVANS: The greatest rituals are, of course, religious. Religion offers a series of rituals to mark the seasons and events in the life of an individual or of a nation.

WINBOLT: How have you managed to combine such diverse callings?

ROOSE-EVANS: I suppose I always had a great sense of spiritual awareness. When I was at Oxford I was in a great crisis. I didn't know whether to be an actor, a writer, a monk, a teacher. I didn't know about being a director. It has taken me all my life to realise that I am all of those things. We are all many people, as you obviously know. So I am a monk, a priest, an actor, a writer and a director. My life remains in theatre, working as a director, but in writing I occasionally draw on my work as a priest.

WINBOLT: You open the book, *Passages of the Soul,* by saying that ritual is one of the keys that can open the doors into the realm of the imagination. One of the things I'm interested in, is to know whether you consider that realm to be on different levels, conscious and unconscious, or specifically of the unconscious?

ROOSE-EVANS: I would say that to allow one's imagination free reign is to activate the unconscious, because we have no control over the images that are going to arise out of it.

Most people, of course, think of the imagination as being something that one makes up, consciously, but that's to do with fantasy.
WINBOLT: And so it seems that ritual is useful precisely because it accesses things at an unconscious level and helps to bring about transformations, that people cannot bring about in other ways - by conscious reasoning or by being told "this is how you do it"?
ROOSE-EVANS: Yes. For example, one of the exercises I do in my workshops is called 'The Journey to the Frontier', where participants make a symbolic journey and are invited to take another person with them as a burden. In real life we all have burdens of one kind or another; the burden of aged or infirm parents, a handicapped child or partner, guilt, fear, and so on. There was one therapist who did the exercise and, because he was locked into a very difficult marriage with his wife pulling against him all the time, he instructed this other person to pull against him. And his was a painful journey to the frontier. He described it beautifully when he said that he knew that this exercise revealed something to him that he would never have realised in any other way. He quoted Joseph Campbell who said, "Marriage is an ordeal. It has nothing to do with being happy. It has to do with being transformed."
WINBOLT: It revealed something about himself, or about his marriage?
ROOSE-EVANS: By doing this exercise he was helped to see his own marriage as an instrument of transformation. Most people think that marriage is about living happily ever after but, as Campbell says, marriage is about transformation. And the partner that life puts you with can be very painful; it can be a martyrdom, but that is what you've got to go through. And, incidentally, you've also got to assist the other person on that journey as well.
WINBOLT: You mentioned Joseph Campbell. He also said that one of the reasons that there is so much violence in

Western culture is that the element of ritual is missing; that there are no rites of initiation now. Therefore young people tend to form gangs and create their own rites of passage. He doesn't elaborate on that, but I'm wondering whether there is a deep need in the human psyche for ritual, one that we don't consciously recognise.

ROOSE-EVANS: Oh yes, I think that there is a need, and you see it coming up more and more today. But people do recognise it consciously. There is one example that comes immediately to my mind.

Two weeks ago a journalist here in London contacted me to ask if I could think of a simple ritual. His mother had died earlier in the year and his father had died long before. Now the family house, where he had lived since the age of ten was being sold. He said that he was finding this very painful because the house has so many meanings for him. It had to be very simple because I didn't know who the people were that he was inviting. I didn't want it to appear pretentious, because people are intimidated by the idea of ritual.

The furniture had all gone, in fact, the grand piano was being carried out just as I was arriving. I gathered from the garden all the flowers I could and placed them in all the rooms with candles burning. About eight o'clock this chap told his friends that I was going to lead a simple ritual to help him to let go of the house. I then simply led everybody through each room, and in each room he spoke of what the room meant to him; his parents' bedroom, the room where he used to study, and so on. This helped him very much.

WINBOLT: He was lucky to have the time to plan the occasion. What about situations where that is not possible. Can such rituals happen spontaneously?

ROOSE-EVANS: Interestingly, a woman present said that when she moved house with her family a few years ago it was her seven-year-old boy - wonderful how children do this - he quite spontaneously ran from room to room kissing the walls, letting go of the house so he could be happy to leave.

WINBOLT: In both those examples we see people finding ways of leaving something behind physically and perhaps geographically. What about life's events where things change around us, the sort of things more readily associated with rituals like births and deaths?
ROOSE-EVANS: Well, people are now creating their own rituals to celebrate the birth of a child, or a loss.
WINBOLT: And these rituals provide something more than the existing forms of baptisms and funerals. Or do people weave their own ideas into a traditional ceremony? For example, I went to a wedding two years ago where the couple had built their own rituals into a Catholic service. It worked well, bringing together a wide variety of people. They all seemed truly involved in the occasion, rather than just witnesses to it.
ROOSE-EVANS: It is interesting when it successfully combines an existing religious ritual with a way of flexibly responding to people's needs. Last autumn I was asked to baptise a little girl of two. The father is English and the mother was from the East and a devout Buddhist. She was dying of cancer and had refused chemotherapy because she'd seen her own mother go through it. I realised the ceremony was to do a number of things. Instead of gathering around the font in the conventional way and handing out cards to everybody, I set up an encampment of chairs in a square. To one side of me was a table with a large shallow basket of autumn leaves - very large, beautiful golden leaves - and then to my left was a bowl of water and candles.

There were people of both nationalities there. I began by holding up one of those leaves and told the story of the Buddha. I said that today we had come together to celebrate two great spiritual traditions, the Buddhist and the Christian. The mother is from the East and Buddhist and the father is English and Christian, and in this child these two traditions come together. And I told the story of the Buddha who, when walking in the park in the autumn, picked up a leaf and said to his disciples, "This leaf represents what I have been able to teach you, but look at all the other leaves on the ground." Similarly, in St John's gospel it says there are not enough books in all the world to record all the things that Jesus said and did. And then I got a small boy of six to go around and hand a leaf to each person there, as a memorial. By this time, the sub-text had got over and people were weeping. They understood it was a leave-taking. There was this beautiful mother, but swollen and with yellow eyes, clearly dying, so I didn't have to say anything, it was apparent.

WINBOLT: That's a nice idea. Leave-taking. And the baptism followed?

ROOSE-EVANS: Yes, and at the moment of the baptism the little girl was very shy. So the three of us, the mother, the girl and I sat down on the floor for the baptism. You see, taking an existing ritual, being flexible and adapting it for a particular human need, enables the great rituals to be rediscovered, found again and new life breathed into them.

WINBOLT: These rituals, though, are recognised as such by the participants. But what if the significance of ritual is something of which most of us are unaware? It seems that there's something in us humans that needs ritual and it therefore fulfils a function of helping us to accept or confront the different stages in our lives, or even the different types of crisis we might meet. That presupposes that a lot of what happens in a ritual is not consciously recognised by the participants as helping them accept and move on. They might recognise it as an occasion, a celebration, but do they know what it signifies?

ROOSE-EVANS: Ritual works on two levels; that of the psychological and that of the spiritual, and sometimes both coincide. But ritual is not to be confused with ceremonial, although ceremonial is part of ritual. Ceremonial is concerned with the externals: arrangements of text, flowers, movement and music. If new rituals are to be effective, they must well up from within the psyche of the participants. When people are given the opportunity and the responsibility for creating their own rituals the results are often quite unexpected and surprising.

WINBOLT: And therapeutic, I should think. Do you think it has a place in the therapeutic process?

ROOSE-EVANS: Yes, I do. I have been through 23 years of Jungian analysis, and that was very rich and fruitful for me. But a lot of therapy is, of course, just sitting opposite another person and talking. I think that we need to use our bodies as well.

WINBOLT: Can you give me some examples of how that can be done?

ROOSE-EVANS: Through enactment, performance. There is an Organisation called *Sesame*which is very interesting. It is taking theatre performance skills which enable people to act out their own myths. So it's a form of therapy through acting out. Because a lot of therapy is just in the head and the body isn't involved. But the guts need to be involved. There is so much wisdom in our bodies if we only knew how to use it. Some rituals can be like dreams in that they have to be lived with. It is not like some puzzle waiting to be solved by the intellect. It is rather a living reality which must be experienced.

WINBOLT: In *Passages of the Soul* you give an example of a dancer who said that she unlocked something in herself through that kind of process.

ROOSE-EVANS: Her name was Carolyn Gracey and I worked with her in New York. She had been distressed by the death of a much-loved teacher, and was trying to create a dance, her own ritual, related to that experience. At first her attempts had been sentimental and melodramatic, more like psychodrama, as though she were too preoccupied with her sentimental response to the bereavement. Then, one day, we had a class discussion where some of the other students attacked the existence of God. She didn't sleep much that night and the next day was very tense. I believe that discussion helped her face a central issue; what is beyond death. As a result her unconscious began to work releasing the essential images she needed. The resulting improvisation was one of the most vivid examples of personal ritual I have ever witnessed. Carolyn herself said that it came out of her "conflict and trouble spilling over into improvisation." In order to work on a subject we need to look at it objectively.

WINBOLT: Is that kind of learning experience, or insight, often achieved through movement? In the example you just gave, Carolyn would have been quite aroused by the events around her, creating a kind of window of opportunity for getting in touch with her emotions spontaneously. In your workshops, for example, do people glimpse things which otherwise they might not do?

ROOSE-EVANS: Yes, it can happen. On the workshop I was running last week we did a lot of work on Shaker rituals, songs and dances...

WINBOLT: Shaker rituals?

ROOSE-EVANS: The Shakers are a remarkable sect which split off from the Quakers and came to be known as the Shaking Quakers, and hence Shakers. They left England and settled in America 250 years ago. I set out to recreate some of their meetings which would employ a great deal of physical movement and dance, as well as shouts, cries and hymns.

I have led a number of workshops on Shakers, and one of the things which moved me very much was a bodily, physical experience. The Shakers begin their meetings for worship by walking up and down, criss-crossing each other, all very intent upon their spiritual journeys. You get, say, 200 people all doing this. And the next stage is, as they pass each other they shove you in the chest and you start to spin and turn and then it goes into leaping and crying out and singing.

WINBOLT: Over what sort of time-scale?

ROOSE-EVANS: Oh, they would meet every evening for three or four hours doing these songs and dancing. And because they were all celibate their sexual energy was obviously being discharged too.

WINBOLT: So in this way, can one learn a sort of acceptance? It makes me think of the way we live life today, pushing to achieve all the time. I read somewhere recently that for some people, when presented with the diagnosis of a major illness, recovery began with acceptance of their condition. Not giving up, but accepting in order to move on.
ROOSE-EVANS: There was a woman who took part recently who was a physiotherapist at a hospice. She said that it moved her because, normally, in real life if somebody thumps you, you want to hit back, but what the Shakers did was to yield and go with the flow. She told me that at the hospice she had observed that the people who had learned to let go and to yield and be flexible in life - in a sense of dying many little deaths - were the ones that died quite easily, whereas those who were more rigid, full of will-power, had the hardest dying because they couldn't let go.
WINBOLT: The example this doctor gave of this acceptance was that most of us live in a state of perpetual confrontation, trying to shape events to suit us, rather than accepting the way of life and adapting to the circumstances as they arise.
ROOSE-EVANS: Yes, in that way, in the Shaker dances, yielding to this thrust and going into a spin, one can see how the body is led into other sequences of movement, each flowing out from the other. It is all very Zen-like. Lao-Tzu, the Chinese philosopher, described how, when a stream meets an obstacle such as a rock, instead of hurling itself at it, as we do when we meet an obstacle, it gently divides itself in two and then continues on the other side with renewed force. His push and yield is central to Shaker philosophy.
WINBOLT: Therefore movement can act as a tool for learning. Many people who haven't had an experience of therapy, or people who don't look at things in that way, in participating they might actually be opening up a part of them to more growth. Is that possible?
ROOSE-EVANS: I think certain people could do this for themselves, Out of their own rich imagination, if you like.

But a lot of people lack that kind of inner light because it has never been developed. They would probably need help.

I remember reading a therapeutic paper where a family had a retarded daughter and they had great difficult in accepting the fact that at the age of 15 or 16 she was going to have to go away for the rest of her life, to a special home, and they were full of guilt about it. So the therapist suggested that at the next meeting they all give this girl something that they have valued very highly and that was most precious to them. At the next meeting the father and mother and brother came up with extraordinary gifts. It was deeply moving. The girl was more than slightly retarded, but even so she was aware of what was happening. And all the family were aware of what they were giving her; they were doing more than just letting her leave. But I think it needed the enabling hand of the therapist to do that.

WINBOLT: But in a workshop situation that help would be there in the form of the person leading the event. Is there the possibility that it can be all the more powerful precisely because some people don't posses the mental gymnastic abilities to make the leap? With the dancer you mentioned earlier, when she tried consciously to conjure up something meaningful, the result was sentimental or melodramatic. If creativity is unconscious and we need to access that creativity it helps to have something that provokes that.

For example, words that are spoken like a nursery rhyme or a verse can be one of the most healing and wonderful things. We were speaking about Joseph Campbell earlier; he said that poetry involves a choice of words that have implications and suggestions that go past the words themselves. So perhaps ritual contains something that goes past the intellect?

ROOSE-EVANS: Well, my mother was not intellectual in any way and perhaps felt once I had become a man there was nothing she could do for me. Whenever I was home she would put a little egg cup filled with tiny flowers on my dresser.

This was a recurring ritual which expressed her need to say, "I love you, you are still my son, I watch over you." We do this constantly in little ways. People aren't aware that even such things as preparing a meal can be a ritual because there's a gift of love in preparing the food and setting it out.
WINBOLT: Because of your background you are speaking very often of rituals in the spiritual, theological sense. For the nourishment of the soul, for the want of a better word, the inner person. In your book you quote Elizabeth Kubler-Ross. You say that in her view funerals are meant simply to gratify the needs of the family and friends to see them through the various stages of mourning, rather than for the soul of the deceased. You say that in our society there is a general conspiracy that death has not occurred.

Are the two views not compatible? That, on the one hand, in the religious sense, the ritual of a funeral can signify a transition from this life to the next, and on the other hand can carry those of us left behind forward on the next stage of our journey? Or is it only for those who are left in mourning, and grieving?
ROOSE-EVANS: You're up against beliefs here. Obviously, as a Christian, if I'm conducting a Christian ritual or if somebody had a deep spiritual inner life and believed in the continuation of that spiritual life hereafter, then that would be woven in to what I said and did, or enabled people to say and do. But if you come up with someone who doesn't believe in anything beyond this existence I couldn't impose my beliefs if I were conducting a funeral. I can't get up and talk about continuity after death because that might anger people and it would be insensitive. If they came to me individually and talked of what you believe, I would share what I believe. But it's only what I believe.
WINBOLT: My question really is, is the ritual of a rite of passage a way of offering the promise of wisdom? Does it open a door to allow people such an insight?
ROOSE-EVANS: Well, yes, there's a Peter Brook quote about

"A great ritual, a fundamental myth is a door, and he who can experience the door within himself passes through it most intensely." I went through such a ritual, or rite of passage, when I was ordained. It was an extraordinary experience which took me by surprise. After a three-day retreat, you are in the cathedral and one by one you go up to the bishop; he's surrounded by about forty clergy, and he presses his hands very hard on your head - then they all do it and you go into a cave of hands. As I went down into this cave of hands, and felt these hands on me, the blood just drained away from me and it was like a shock of ice cold water. I was shaken to the very core of my being, and knew that something had happened to me which could never be erased. If you have that kind of experience you have opened a door into an inner realm which will then lead you on to other doors and to other realms.

WINBOLT: You said earlier that "There is so much wisdom in our bodies if we only knew how to use it". Do you think that that sort of experience can act as a door into inner wisdom?

ROOSE-EVANS: I wouldn't use the word 'wisdom'. I think I'd rather use the word 'knowledge'. During this last workshop I often read the poem Ithaca, which has the line "on your journey to Ithaca, visit all these different places, learn and learn from those who have knowledge"; and it talks about not hurrying the voyage, but letting it last a long time and only to arrive at Ithaca when you are old, full of riches. And when you arrive you will find that Ithaca has nothing to give you, but she has not defrauded you; with the great wisdom you have gained you will by now know what Ithaca means.

So the wisdom is at the end of the journey, rather than the beginning. You first have to start out on it.

WINBOLT: You frequently use the idea of a journey in your workshops. Is that in the sense of a pilgrimage, a literal, physical journey, or does it mean a journey within?

ROOSE-EVANS: A ritual may involve an actual journey,

which can be short or long, as in a pilgrimage. A pilgrim proceeds to a faraway place in search of a shared adventure and finally returns home. In short, a journey en route to his or her roots.

WINBOLT: How do you invoke the idea of starting out on such a journey?

ROOSE-EVANS: In the exercises that I do with people, they begin always from the point of centring or focusing to allow an initial image to occur. For instance, my hand starts to vibrate and so I have to do something about that. That's my first image, the vibrating hand, and I have to try perhaps to control it and then I will see where that hand is leading me. In the exercise of journeys to the frontier which I use, it might be that for some reason I start with another image, say that of a crippled foot. Then I have to follow that image through, rather than allow the mind to keep chopping and changing the images all the time. The basis of it is quite close to what Jung called the use of visualisation. It is these key images that will lead one on a kind of exercise. I am not talking about conventional rituals or domestic rituals at the moment; I am just talking about a specific type of exercise. It is possible for a very simple exercise to trigger off a deep need or image in the individual. When this need can be dealt with in terms of ritual, and when the ritual really works - it's not often, of course, that it happens - it goes like that! There's a release. There is still pain and grieving, of course, but you might spend a year or two in analysis working through such a problem to arrive at the same point.

WINBOLT: So then, this can lead to transformation. In your book you say that rituals can mark a transformation, or transition, but you have just mentioned that it doesn't often happen. Do many people tell you about such experiences when doing these exercises?

ROOSE-EVANS: I never ask people to talk about it, but if they want to they can. If it becomes a transforming experience then it is a true rite of passage. Otherwise it is a fruitful exercise of perhaps the more conscious imagination. Perhaps it's closer to day-dreaming; the imagination is at work but is not actually transforming. It is still fruitful though, and there is something to meditate on at the end.

WINBOLT: Which can help people grow in their understanding of things and themselves. Is that what attracts people to workshops such as yours?

ROOSE-EVANS: People are drawn into such workshops because there is in them a hunger for something that they cannot find elsewhere. A psychotherapist wrote to me saying that her years of training had been mainly a conscious, verbal process, and that now she "needed a new knowing." She said that in spite of years of good therapy she still had something inside her that was wounded and which controlled most of her responses.

WINBOLT: And how easily do people join in with that process? Earlier, in talking about the ritual for leaving the house, you said that you were careful not to appear pretentious. There is a sense in some of the exercises that you mention, for people who are not used to approaching things in that way, that they might appear a little theatrical, pretentious even. Have you had any of that in your workshops, or does everyone accept it and join in comfortably?

ROOSE-EVANS: It has happened that I have intervened during my workshop exercises if I thought someone was having trouble doing the exercises authentically. I remember one person who was walking towards the 'frontier' much more quickly than the other participants, in a deliberate sort of way. I felt she was being far too conscious about it, intellectualising the process. She was most put out when I suggested she do it again, but I insisted. I don't think she gained a lot from that particular exercise.

WINBOLT: The image of a frontier can refer to our own personal boundaries and limitations as much as the more external ones presented by life. As you have said in your book, it may stand for the frontier between childhood and adolescence, innocence and experience, virgin to woman, boy to man; it may remind us of external frontiers between faiths, groups and cultures, or any number of other images.

ROOSE-EVANS: The frontier exercise is incredibly powerful. It is draining to watch. It's like hearing endless confessions. It can be powerful. What happens to people is the experience. Sometimes people come to the frontier and find they cannot cross it.

One woman just recently, a therapist I know, got to the frontier but was unable to go further. She was beating against the wall, but her beating was very feeble. She really couldn't deal with it. I know what she is going through in her real life and this was very painful for her, because it made her fully confront the impossible situation she is in. All she could do was, in a sense, go back to base and wait for another day. Which is like consulting the I Ching, which often says the idea is right, but the timing is wrong.

WINBOLT: How does one recognise a ritual? What are the essential elements that we can recognise and how can we know when we are involved in one?

ROOSE-EVANS: I would have thought that it is rare for a ritual to happen spontaneously because there have to be structures and parameters. If, for example, you are going to the funeral service of somebody you love very dearly, it has to be clearly structured or else people could break down hopelessly. So they know there is a perimeter to the whole thing. There is a beginning, a middle and an end.

WINBOLT: And yet the personal rituals can just happen; you mentioned the ones we use each day to enable us to come to terms with events in our lives.

ROOSE-EVANS: Yes, at a personal level a ritual can happen spontaneously, but I think a lot of people are unconscious of it. Obviously to put flowers on a grave is a very important ritual, but I should have thought that a lot of people perhaps don't realise that they are performing such rituals.

WINBOLT: As many of the true rituals in our society are

disappearing, how can we ensure that ritual is restored to our culture?

ROOSE-EVANS: All that any of us can do, you in your small corner and I in mine, is do what we can and that ripples out amongst the people we meet. And there are a lot of such people like us and a lot of centres, like mine in Wales , and others. There's a lot going on and ripples are going out. It can't be a mass movement, it's something that slowly filters through, so it's a slow process and will take a long time and many lives.

WINBOLT: So we come back to the beginning of a journey.

ROOSE-EVANS: We are all on the same journey. The more conscious each of us can become, I don't mean self-conscious but truly conscious of what we are about and why we are behaving in this way or that way, the deeper our journeys are going to be anyway, and the richer the rituals when we come to them.

Where the rainbow ends - the collapse of civilization

Anne Glyn-Jones spent nine years researching how and why civilizations decline. ***Ivan Tyrrell*** *talks to her about her alarming conclusions.*

IVAN TYRRELL: In your book, *Holding up a Mirror - How Civilizations Decline,* you describe our culture as one which "has run its course, which is morally, aesthetically and spiritually bankrupt." You also stated that "our woes are the direct and logical result of the belief that the physical universe is the only reality that does or can exist; and that truth resides solely in the analysis and understanding of that 'reality'."

Well, the 'woes' are what therapists are usually trying to deal with in one form or another, which is why I thought our readers would like me to interview you.

ANNE GLYN-JONES: I foresee a problem. As a therapist, you surely would approach this topic from the point of view of the individual, whereas I approach it with a predominant interest in society as a whole, and that might make our discussion difficult.

TYRRELL: Surely it shouldn't. Just because there is more than one way of looking at a topic does not make the different approaches mutually exclusive. One great human trait is our ability to change focus in space and time. Surely a greater understanding of the whole picture helps us understand the individual and *vica versa.* Therapists are trying, after all, to deal with a rising tide of anger, anxiety and stress-related disorders - depression has seen a tenfold increase since 1945. In my experience all good therapists are interested in the larger picture too - anthropology, sociology, history, philosophy and, above all, in meaning. How could it be otherwise?

GLYN-JONES: Society *is* composed of individuals, but not all equally - there are dominant, opinion-forming individuals and groups, and sheepish people and groups who go with the tide. It is the former who determine the society's cultural evolution.

TYRRELL: Yes, which is worrying. As you pointed out, when Lloyds launched Access cards in October 1972, they used the slogan "Access takes the waiting out of wanting", which disturbed people who had been led to believe that an inability to postpone gratification was one of the hallmarks of a psychopath! As a culture, we now seem out of control. We waste energy and time chasing possessions, money, power, sexual gratification and ever more extreme forms of emotional excitement. All natural enough perhaps, since greed is built into all living things, but we seem to have discovered how to override nature's checks and balances.

In your book you show vividly how the 'arts' and the entertainment and advertising industries today use great ingenuity to gratify an apparently insatiable greed for stimulation. And you also describe how expressions of pornographic depravity and cruel, mindless violence have rapidly become commonplace in films, plays, books, magazines, computer games, in playgrounds and on the streets.

You describe how this is one of the symptoms of a particular type of society. Another symptom is that social responsibility becomes more and more subsumed to individuals' desires, however base those desires may be, and however much stress this causes. Is there a pattern in all this? I've long suspected that this has all happened before, which is why I found your book so interesting. Can we start by describing the pattern you believe you can see?

GLYN-JONES: My approach was inspired by Pitirim Sorokin who experienced at first hand social theory in action in the Russian Revolution, which, incidently, nearly cost him his life. After various traumatic adventures he managed to escape to America where he devoted the rest of his life to working out his own interpretation of why societies change.

Sorokin, who founded the Department of Sociology at Harvard, disagreed with the founding fathers of sociology, like Max Weber, who believed that, if it were to qualify as a science, sociology must strictly avoid value judgements. On the contrary, he considered that an understanding of human societies could not begin without an assessment of what people cared about, and how that influenced their activities. He sought to analyse the dominant temper of the age across many different civilizations, from ancient Babylon to 20th century America.

TYRRELL: The great problem with that, surely, is that research into what makes a society tick cannot take place in a laboratory like the physical sciences can.

GLYN-JONES: That's true, his type of hypotheses are tested through the process of statistical correlation. This requires the amassing of a vast quantity of factual data. Sorokin recruited an army of collaborators and, with their help, analysed the manifestations of the human spirit in different periods and among different peoples, as revealed in painting, sculpture, literature, architecture and music - not in aesthetic terms but in terms of social content. For instance: were the subjects religious or secular? Aristocratic or common people? How was nudity portrayed - erotically or aesthetically? What social priorities did literature express - duty or comfort? He worked through developments in philosophy and politics, in science and technology, and he looked at the way changing attitudes were reflected in changes in the law and in the delineation of crime. And he also examined the scale and intensity of wars and civil commotion.

These vast labours provided the material for his *Social and Cultural Dynamics*. The whole work runs to some 3,000 pages.

Before publication was complete, however, the Second World War broke out and, by the time it was over, there was not much interest in sweeping analyses of society at large other than Marxism, a creed for which Sorokin accurately foresaw only a limited future.

Sorokin's work was soon forgotten. But it doesn't deserve to be. In the 50 years since his theories were first published, events have justified his predictions at every level.

TYRRELL: As I understand it, his idea was that civilization changed, ultimately, because of what its opinion formers *believed.* Isn't this a very different idea from all those theories that depend on climate, trade, race and all those other aspects that could be influencing and changing societies?

GLYN-JONES: Yes. Sorokin became convinced that what people ultimately believe about what is true finally filters through every aspect of their civilization. Moreover, every civilization which swims into our ken can be understood more thoroughly when we understand what they fundamentally believed. And he classified the type of beliefs in three ways.

In the early stage of civilizations, for example, men and women were very dominated by anxiety and the need to placate whatever the unseen powers were that seemed to them to be ultimately responsible for their lives. Their anxieties were very basic ones; would the crops ripen, will the river flood, will the children look after you in your old age, or will disease, drought, famine or enemies destroy the village. I think that is why those civilizations were deeply religious. Everything was sacred - stones, streams, rivers, trees, sacred groves - all belonging to the gods who must not be upset. They were trying to keep the peace with the ultimate dynamics of the world.

TYRRELL: Was this, do you think, why their moral codes were so black-and-white?

GLYN-JONES: Yes. Their religion was largely ritualistic and propitious. They felt they must not put a foot wrong because, if they did, the whole tribe might suffer. So the morality was strict and the art symbolic - the gods mattered all the time and you couldn't portray them as human beings, you could only portray them in symbolic form and there is no art other than that. Art was seen purely as a form of worship.

Such a society Sorokin called "ideational", where people tend to describe the experience of the senses as illusory, believing instead that reality is immaterial, transcendental, eternal and unchanging. In an ideational society truth comes through revelation; its interpreters are the priests and prophets. Proposed changes to the existing way of doing things are tested by reference to sacred books and traditions. Men and women do not feel restricted by supposed biological limits, for there is a strong belief in the power of mind over matter. Fire-walking or yogic demonstrations such as remaining alive without food or air are products of this point of view. Miracles are taken for granted - they are a logical outcome of such attitudes; and sick or distressed believers will place much more faith in miracles than in medicine. Where the 'other' world counts for so much, frugality in daily life, even asceticism, is admired and emulated.

This is not a very comfortable society to live in. There are contemporary examples of this extreme model such as fundamentalist Islamic societies and similar Christian cults that emerge from time to time.

TYRRELL: What then is the second evolutionary stage of a typical culture?

GLYN-JONES: Gradually people become more humane. They begin to value the material world around them more. They still think the world is a really dangerous place to live in but they also develop a certain capacity to manipulate it.

TYRRELL: In fact, rigidity starts to break down.

GLYN-JONES: It does. Sorokin called this the "idealist" phase where people develop a more humanistic attitude to one another and, at the same time, begin to take a bolder approach to manipulating the natural world - which they no longer see as entirely sacred. They become less worried about 'unseen powers', but still believe firmly in them - and those powers are the arbiters of their morality, values and aesthetic ideas.

Then some of the best minds in the community start to question this natural world and how it works. (They called it "natural philosophy" in the old days. We call it science.) They are no longer totally absorbed with the question of the right relationship with the gods. They're looking at the world around them as well.

Such a society is less worried by a sense of impotence in the face of occult forces and more confident about its ability to control its environment. It can dare to relax and enjoy the material world. Then attitudes towards human aspirations become more gentle. The unseen powers begin to be seen as positively benign and human happiness becomes a legitimate objective, though they still believe it is only achievable within the moral framework established by the transcendent world.

TYRRELL: So, the material world begins to be valued for its own sake, for its beauty and bounteousness, and its potential begins to be explored.

GLYN-JONES: Yes. But while the material world becomes accepted as real and important, it's not seen as having any authority in the realm of values, either moral or aesthetic.

Idealist art expresses unchanging qualities of permanent serenity. It dares to express the unseen world and humanise it. That's why you find, in the twelfth century Christian madonnas, for instance, a beautiful, but not erotic, woman. She is not an abstract symbol. Byzantine paintings, for example, are very, *very* still. They take you beyond this world. They were not intended to be life-like depictions. You're invited beyond, into another world. That's the message they are trying to get across.

This "Idealist" world was, of course, Sorokin's favourite because he felt it was a beautiful blend of the material and non-material.

TYRRELL: How do you mean?

GLYN-JONES: Well, such societies have the technology to put up the Parthenon in Greece, for example, or raise the exquisite domes on Islamic mosques or build the great Gothic

cathedrals, but, at the same time, they retained the powerful feeling that what ultimately matters is God.
TYRRELL: What is the third stage?
GLYN-JONES: The "sensate" phase. As confidence grows, and human self-consciousness and enjoyment of the material world grows, so the sensate, as Sorokin calls it, side of life becomes more and more important.
By sensate he meant two things. One, as you would expect, is what we enjoy and experience through our senses. The other, and more important, revolves round the idea that all truth is apprehended only through the five senses - what you can see, hear, smell, taste and touch - and the use of reason. At this stage of civilization we are urged on to invent all sorts of ways of extending what our senses can do, whether it is with a microscope, telescope or, as in our own times, the exploration of radio and electromagnetic waves, and so on, which previous civilizations couldn't do.

Reason is a very powerful influence in idealistic societies too, but much less so because superstition may still reign supreme in the general population. In idealist societies human reason is brought to bear and their philosophers are very keen that it should be.

In a sensate society, however, there is a move towards, not merely the *use* of reason, but *a reliance on rationality to the exclusion of everything else*. That means that, ultimately, reason, working from what the five senses input, is seen as the only avenue to truth that anybody is prepared to accept as valid.
TYRRELL: And where does that lead us?
GLYN-JONES: To the sort of society where 'gut' reactions, intuition, prophecy, revelation, sacred books, tradition, what our ancestors valued and said, become less and less important and, eventually, are discarded as forms of superstition.
TYRRELL: What does that mean, for example, to the world of medicine?

GLYN-JONES: When society becomes mainly concerned with what human beings can manipulate in the environment, medicine virtually stops asking ethical questions. Perhaps that's going a little bit too far to make a point here, but, in modern medicine, we have examples of things that science can do for us that we have progressively accepted.
TYRRELL: I don't understand.
GLYN-JONES: Well, for example, initially there was discomfort about heart transplants but, once it was shown it *could* be done, then it *was* done. And people forget that, once upon a time, not so long ago, society believed that every heart transplant involved a moral decision.
TYRRELL: Yes, I remember that. There was a time when heart transplants were first possible, perhaps only a few months though, when people were saying, "Should we be doing this or not...?"
GLYN-JONES: Yes, and, in a purely sensate society, people almost cease to ask that question. We have gone progressively through artificial insemination by a husband, that was all right - then we said, "well, if the husband can't produce a baby, let's go for artificial insemination by donor." And that raised a great many ethical problems but we overcame them. In effect we now say, "If we can do it, it must be all right."

That has taken us to where we are at the moment - in-vitro-fertilization and the proposed use of aborted foetus eggs to generate new life. There are already voices in the scientific and medical profession saying it is absurd to stop here. The argument goes that, by using these eggs, women who would not otherwise have the joy of giving birth to a baby, because there are not enough donor eggs around, can achieve happiness. And that is a demonstration of how the dominant criterion of what is right action has changed from what the gods want to what we want.
TYRRELL: I see. The question, "What is it that will make human beings happy?" is a completely alien idea to either an ideational or, substantially, to an idealist society, where

they would be more preoccupied with the duty owed to something greater than themselves.
GLYN-JONES: Yes. In a fully sensate society that idea has completely gone.
You get an idea of this if you compare the old catechisms, "Why am I here? I am here to do my duty to God." "What is my duty to God? To love him to serve him," etc. These old catechisms are completely superseded by the dominant document of the modern age, which is the American Declaration of Independence, where God gets a little look-in, but not very much, because he has given us the right to life, liberty and the pursuit of happiness. This is a tremendously significant document, but one which has had results that I think have led to a great deal of unhappiness. This, I know, is of concern to therapists trying to deal with individual distress or breakdown.

The reason why the American Declaration of Independence misdirected us is partly that, the more you pursue happiness, the less you find it. You discover happiness only as a by-product of pursuing something else.
TYRRELL: I can see that the three types of civilization you describe, the ideational, idealistic and sensate, is a useful way of studying the history of cultures but, in reality, is it as simple as that? When animism and shamanism, for example, are superseded as cultures become more complex and organised religions develop, we find that, what we normally like to think of as "higher" civilizations and religions are really no more than a veneer. Primitive, magical forms of thinking still survive underneath into the modern world. Much behaviour seems to me to be still largely governed by primitive beliefs, magical thinking and animal reactions.
GLYN-JONES: No society of any size or complexity is a pure manifestation of any one of these world views. Exponents of all three, and variants of them, exist in all societies, though unevenly distributed among different social groups and different historical epochs.

TYRRELL: People, especially representatives of institutions like bishops, judges and politicians, are happy to pontificate about civilized behaviour - "this is civilized" and "that's uncivilized" - but I don't think it's that simple. It's all mixed up. The apparently most civilized among us can, when the context is slightly manipulated, be shown to behave like primitives. Likewise, truly advanced people can live in a sensate society like ours and remain invisible to the people around them.

GLYN-JONES: Yes, and we also change our usage of the word 'civilized'. There were very great civilizations in the past which were based, for instance, on slavery. But, by today's standards, we would say they were uncivilized because we now believe exploiting slaves is not civilized behaviour.

TYRRELL: What do you think about institutions as a mark of civilization?

GLYN-JONES: What kind of institutions are you thinking of?

TYRRELL: Well, the churches, monarchy, parliamentary institutions, legal and educational institutions. Many people are proud of these institutions, trust them, boast about them - a politician's stock-in-trade phrase when an institution is being criticized is to say something like, "our legal/ parliamentary/educational system is the envy of the world." But, in a way, our institutions are a symptom of failure, not of civilization. Institutions are only in place because people are *not* civilized. They are the social equivalent of barbed wire that's used to contain wild animals - they are there to stop us being completely degenerate, destructive and out-of-control. That's how I see it.

GLYN-JONES: That's very interesting.

TYRRELL: Institutions evolved in an attempt to contain our excesses, just as prisons are needed to contain dangerous, antisocial criminals. Institutions are only in place because most people can't be relied on to be honest, fair and humane towards one another, or act from a body of real knowledge about *how* to behave.

GLYN-JONES: Yes, I think there is a lot of truth in that. And the fascinating thing is that it's a very old intuition. When the ancient Greeks, in the third century BC, entered their sensate phase, the Greek Stoics, who, against the grain, were trying to promote calm, quiet, dispassionate, reasoned and humane behaviour, said the same thing. They looked at their Roman conquerors, who were pretty incorruptible, didn't take bribes, were disciplined and loyal, and compared them with their fellow Greek citizens who were the exact opposite - untrustworthy, effete, immoral, taking back-handers whenever they could and so on. The Stoics wondered why the Romans were so superior and came to the conclusion that it was the Roman religion that made Romans behave better. This was because, at that stage of their history, Romans were actually rather afraid of the gods and what would happen to them if they didn't behave. Now, although the Stoics didn't believe in the Roman religion, they could see the result of not having strong institutions in the collapsing Greek civilization all around them. They came to the conclusion that religious institutions are necessary because people are such tempestuous mobs who can't govern themselves - and so they've got to be governed.

Today the doctrine of human rights has set human being against human being with more vehemence than ever before. People feel now that they have a 'moral' justification for whatever they do, because they are all now referring to what they consider to be their rights as *individuals.*

TYRRELL: Yes, and of course it falls down horribly because you can't have rights for individuals overriding rights for larger groups of people.

GLYN-JONES: Exactly. That's what we have lost. And this extreme individualism is a major component of the breakdown of culture.

When we talk about the influence of religion on society, we have to remember that there are many different religions, doctrinally. Sorokin's "ideational" society is simply one in which people feel they owe an overriding obedience to an immaterial authority greater than themselves. The specific commands may be, in the eyes of another religion, horrific, like the Aztecs ripping the beating hearts from sacrificial victims to ensure the sun rises tomorrow. Or the current Taliban closure of schools that educate women in Afghanistan - religion used, as it so often is, to consolidate some group in secular power. Nevertheless, my analysis shows that, once the sense of obedience to some Greater Good goes, and people live for themselves, hedonism takes over. Even in Russia, where for 70 years the whole system preached a gospel of service to the cause of the workers, it became obvious with the collapse of 1989 that it was only repression that had maintained a semblance of social cohesion. No compelling loyalty to any unselfish obligation was being inculcated, and problems of self-indulgence, crime, drunkenness, family breakdown and so on were already evident before 1989.

I doubt, though, if in any society a majority has had a lively, personal, living awareness of the transcendental realities in which the "ideational" and "idealist" civilizations claim to be grounded. What *really* influences people is the accepted popular culture, 'the done thing', particularly as encapsulated in the society's laws and traditions. It was much easier for people to feel part of this culture when it was grounded in festivals celebrating the seasonal round. But urban people have no such anchor. Once the opinion formers - philosophers in the long run, artists in the quite short run - lose their faith, and embark on the obvious temptations of the pursuit of individualism and its associated relativist morality, the collapse of the old order, both in conduct and in law, is quite rapid, especially when it is accompanied - as in later materialist societies it usually is - by extensive settlement of outsiders whose social 'myths' as to 'the done thing' are rather different.

TYRRELL: Can we talk more specifically about our society today. A lot of people who read *The Therapist* are engaged in dealing with stress-related problems of one sort or another - family breakdowns and so forth - and are concerned to understand about modern day pressures. What stage do you think it's at now?

GLYN-JONES: Well, fairly late. Fairly late in terms of the dynamics of degeneration. But we should remember that a society can be degenerate and unpleasant to live in because of the levels of crime, insecurity, unhappiness and uncertainty, but, at the same time, if it can keep its economy going and is not conquered by an outside group, it can struggle on for quite a long time. Greece didn't struggle on for very long because it had Rome on its doorstep disliking the Greek anarchy and piracy that was affecting Roman trade. The Romans just decided to stamp down hard on them and knock them into shape as it were.

But then, of course, Rome degenerated. However, it managed to stagger on in a highly decadent condition for a remarkably long time while the barbarian tribes organized themselves.

I was surprised as I looked at different cultures that having a superior technology does not save a sensate culture from collapse. Greek technology was superior to Roman and Roman technology was superior to the barbarians. But they all fell. And we can see a hint of that today in the way our Western, technically superior, cultures have been expelled from Somaliland, Afghanistan, Vietnam and so on. Despite considerably more advanced Western technology, our sensate cultures couldn't cope, obsessed with individualism as they are, with an idealist enemy prepared to die for a greater good.

TYRRELL: So, we can hang on for a long while, despite being so degenerate...?

GLYN-JONES: Yes, as long as we don't find ourselves up against a highly disciplined, cohesive enemy, and at the moment it looks as if we're not.

At present the threats to our existence are internal rather than external. We can go on for a long time without a revolution that causes something new to happen. That's not to say we will be living in a particularly estimable level of civilization. Our art may become so degenerate that future generations will be completely uninterested in it. Life may become increasingly insecure. But the great threat to us is that we have a society which is devoted to the pursuit of happiness, seen largely in material terms - economic well-being - *and we shall fail to deliver the goods.* I'm not even talking about other sorts of happiness now, but just economic goods.

TYRRELL: How come? We've never had so much materially.

GLYN-JONES: Because the financial costs of policing, arson, vandalism and family breakdown destroy the very *raison-d'être* of materialist societies, namely, rising living standards. That's always happened in the past. Down here, where I live in the South West, there is a hospital which has just had to switch £80,000 into security fencing, which it would otherwise have used for patient care; there are umpteen examples like that. I read just the other day that the cost of crime to small businesses in the last 12 months was £1.5 billion. They have already reached the stage where the expense of screens to stop ram raiders, burglar alarms, in-store closed circuit television to combat shop lifting, store detectives and so on is at such a high level they can no longer make a profit. They can't even pay for insurance, the cost of crime is so great, particularly in the inner cities. The cost of more policing and prisons is crippling.

Look at what's happening in the schools! The amount of finance they are now having to put into security is enormous - all over the country.

Down here in Exeter, four years ago, the Municipal Mutual Insurance Company went broke. Overnight local authorities found they were uninsured. Fire engines and ambulances had to be shut up in their stations. They couldn't risk putting them on the streets uninsured. And what broke MMI was mainly insurance claims for school theft and school arson.

One in eight schools are being set on fire every year by out-of-control children. And computers and other electronic equipment are disappearing from schools at a rapidly increasing rate.

TYRRELL: Yes - even our little village primary school had its one and only, brand new computer stolen within 24 hours of it being installed.

GLYN-JONES: That's now typical. You also have a vast amount of fraud and theft going on in high places, and not just fraud by company directors that average citizens may be practising, but huge fraud in government, in the National Health Service, the Civil Service, in Pension Funds, in City institutions - many being fined for malpractice now - and the cost of all this corruption comes out of people's hard earned income and savings. Even pension funds aren't safe.

The degree of theft from churches, National Trust property, from people's cars, boats, houses, gardens - all of this is economically diminishing because, although you may be able to afford to replace stolen or destroyed items, or claim insurance money for it, the insurance puts the premiums up and we all have to pay for that. It's got so bad now that many people think nothing of regularly making false claims on their insurance!

All this makes it more difficult to achieve the economic advance that governments like to promise us, quite apart from all the other problems we are up against now.

TYRRELL: It's as if we're running faster and faster but just going backwards.

GLYN-JONES: Moreover, going backwards on the down escalator!

Another reason we shall fail to deliver the goods is permissiveness. For instance, state welfare payments for single parents are going up and up. When people say that this doesn't matter, "people are just not bothering to go through the marriage ceremony but are mostly living in pretty stable relationships", it just isn't true. Recent research showed that now 60 per cent of unmarried single mothers have never lived with the father of their baby.

There's a vast level of costs involved. We just don't know to what extent the disturbed and delinquent children of broken families are adding to our costs, the costs of looking after them and paying for the damage that they do to other people.

TYRRELL: And are these all signs that the majority of us are living for immediate gratification of the senses?

GLYN-JONES: Yes. And we see this everywhere. For example, nobody is expected to be able to control themselves sexually any longer. If you fall in love, that's it. You can do anything you want. But at the beginning of this century there were millions of women across Europe left single after the First World War. Nobody expected them to go off and break up other people's marriages just because they hadn't got a man of their own. And yet now anybody who hasn't got a sexual partner of their own finds another one, and if they happen to 'fall in love' with someone who's married, never mind what damage it does to the husband or wife or children left behind. Love is now supposed to be a completely irresistible impulse. Well, the Greeks of the classical period considered that sort of love a disease - a form of madness.

TYRRELL: I'm quite sure it is. Love is a trance state. "Love is blind," as they say. Of course this is where the arts and entertainment draw much material from because relationships endlessly fascinate.

How do you see the three different views of the world reflected in the culture of today? I'm intrigued whether you think that the arts actually help to create the sensate society or whether they just reflect it.

GLYN-JONES: It depends what art it is. These three different views of the world can be traced in the evolution of law and custom; in the relationship between religion and science; in attitudes to technology and to the way we exploit the material world. It's also observable in the dominant philosophies -

political, moral and metaphysical; and in the way in which different societies behave. But, above all, they are made manifest in the arts.

Controversy over whether dramatic entertainment is simply reflecting life; responding to a market in sensational taste; or initiating value changes that are impinging on real life, is raging now. I think that the *visual* arts, particularly film, television and theatre, very readily put a stamp of approval on behaviour. They validate actions and behaviour in a much stronger way than if you only read about them. Now we see the public taste for explicit sex and violence evolving with all the enthusiasm of the Roman amphitheatre. And there is no doubt this spills out onto the streets.

The emotional damage done to victims of criminals, muggers, rapists and murderers is incalculable, a state of affairs which victim support groups try to ameliorate; but some sufferers are destroyed by the loss of their trust in fellow human beings. An 86-year-old woman, though unhurt when her handbag containing only £4 was snatched, never smiled again and in a month she was dead. It's the elderly who remember a very different social atmosphere who are probably the most affected. The philosopher Leopold Kohr died in February 1994 a broken-hearted man shortly after the fourteenth burglary of his Gloucestershire home that left all his papers ransacked. "They have finally murdered my career," he said, "I do not think I can begin writing again."

TYRRELL: Some people say, though, that it's fear of crime, not crime itself, that is the real enemy.

GLYN-JONES: Yes. I've noticed *The Times*, in particular, never ceases to point out, each time the Home Office releases the latest crime figures, that conditions are far worse in other countries; that the apparent increase in crime reflects unreliable statistics rather than real increases; and that in any case the statistical likelihood of being a victim of violence remains low. Whilst it's true that Home Office surveys reveal a huge discrepancy between crime and reported crime - not, in itself, a particularly consoling discovery - leaving open the possibility that apparent increases may be due largely to more reporting and recording, anecdote and personal experience convince most people that they are in greater peril than they used to be.

A low statistical risk influences perception less than the extreme nastiness of the incidents that do occur. For example, householders faced with minor vandalism in their localities hesitate to protest, remembering the couple on a South London housing estate who, in 1989, perished in the flames when their flat was set on fire following their complaint about their neighbours' loud music. A train passenger who had the gall to remonstrate with fellow passengers for putting their feet on the seat upholstery was stabbed through the heart. A father-of-three, who challenged 20 young vandals on a Cardiff estate in June 1993, was kicked to death. In Christchurch, Dorset, a month later, a 56-year-old man who asked a group of teenagers to quieten down had his teeth knocked out after being kicked to the ground. A man trying to stop a burglary at a neighbour's home near Portsmouth had his leg broken in 6 places; his assailants included a 13-year-old girl. I could go on.

In 1993, three appalling crimes confirmed, in many people's estimation, the connection between the collapse of civilized standards and the influence of popular entertainment. The abduction, slow sexual torture and murder of two-year-old James Bulger by two ten-year-olds held up to the British public a stark and brutal reflection of what sort of conduct the nation was now breeding. Both perpetrators were video addicts whose first port-of-call after the murder was a video shop. A number of details in the case reflected incidents in a 'video nasty', *Child's Play 3*, which was known to have been seen by the father of one of the murderers, though it was denied that the child had seen it. Shortly after their conviction there was a trial of 6 adults accused of the torture, sexual and otherwise, of a 16-year-old girl whom they finally disposed of by setting on fire. Unexpectedly the victim lived long enough to give police details of her tormentors. *Child's Play 3* featured overtly in the torture. In neither case did the police impugn the video, though others did. Police did, however, link the kicking to death of the man in Cardiff who remonstrated with the gang for vandalism with the American film *Juice*, which the youths had been watching. Commentators tend to describe such violence as "mindless", but it is no more 'mindless' than enjoying a pint of beer. Destruction and the infliction of suffering is now seen by many people as pleasurable.

The argument about whether saturation in a depraved culture produces adult or juvenile criminals, lances criminal propensities, or is a symptom of wider influences which are just manifesting themselves in our culture, will go on and on no doubt. But, if the cultural celebration of criminality is primarily a symptom, it does not follow that it should not be subjected to controls, just as medical symptoms are. But it does mean that, unless the underlying dynamics of the disease are confronted, the controls will be no more than plasters on a sick organism. Violence and pornography are beamed from satellites, filter by phone line along computer networks and seep through computer games sold to children. This is very nasty material indeed, and it is more prevalent and much easier to find than most people imagine.

TYRRELL: This is quite different than the effect of stories from the oral traditions, which are often quite lurid, or the power of Classical Greek theatre, isn't it?

GLYN-JONES: Yes. It's interesting that the Greeks would not even allow on-stage violence. They dealt with the most appalling atrocities in their drama, but they were always reported from offstage. The audience didn't see them acted out in front of their eyes.

TYRRELL: Your work is primarily concerned with the collapse of the social order, and this is precisely why I think it relates to our interest in therapy for disturbed and unhappy people. What do you think about this?

GLYN-JONES: I didn't specifically explore this in my book, but my highly unfashionable standpoint is implicit in it, if not explicit. My own belief, and it is one I've come to through harsh personal experience, is that we grossly overestimate our own importance, and make our situation much worse by talking the language of rights, which can only leave us resentful, dissatisfied and in conflict with others.

One of the few things on which I agree with the Marxists is in regarding the language of individual rights as corrosive of social cohesion, as well as being productive of much personal distress. Of course that doesn't mean I condone the system of oppression, the Gulag, in the USSR or anywhere else. But I try to phrase all statements about conduct between human beings - or human beings and animals, come to that - in the language of 'duties'. Old-fashioned Christianity used to talk about the 'Vale of Tears', and this at least helped people to accept such misfortunes as bereavement and acute disappointment. Today, with the foolish shibboleth of universal happiness, we've bred a population raw with frustration and - yes - resentful rage. And modern Christianity, with its overemphasis on how important each one of us is in the sight of God, and how much he loves us all etc., totes faggots to the fire...

TYRRELL: ...adding the stench of hypocrisy to the tyranny of individualism.

Do you see any hopeful signs that we might come out of this sensate phase without a complete collapse?

GLYN-JONES: The current Green movement is interesting in throwing down the gauntlet to materialism and hedonism - well, two gauntlets really. One is from those talking the language of expediency: we must control ourselves in order not to wreak damage on ourselves and our descendants. The other talks in transcendental terms about the ultimate unity of all living things, an attitude commanding us to regard creation as a sort of sacred trust. The first proposition brooks dispute - "I've no children ... why should I forego pleasure on

behalf of other people's descendants?" etc. The second is absolute, and to me much more compelling.
TYRRELL: The trouble is, talking about "the ultimate unity of all living things" often makes people feel they are doing something without them getting any nearer knowing what *can* and *needs* to be done.

It seems to me that, unless we bring our acquisitional instincts under conscious control soon, we face extinction. We have no choice but to learn to be economical about satisfying the base greeds that largely motivate us and determine much of our behaviour. This is quite different from saying, as conventional religious people so often do, that we must "eliminate all desire" or "own nothing". The important thing is to satisfy these basic needs with the minimum gratification necessary in order to free ourselves. Then perhaps we can begin to operate in other ways.

But, at the moment, these basic drives - all aspects of greed - dominate our lives. We are not in charge of ourselves while these powerful instincts are running riot, causing chaos and destruction wasting our time and energy. We are making our own and other people's lives miserable or impossible. You describe this so well in your book - how we become cruel and insensitive as our greed blinds us to other people's needs.

If we have a destiny, this is not the way to fulfil it. And the first step to improving the situation must surely be to bring these instinctual drives under control, in other words - to gain freedom from them.
GLYN-JONES: I'm afraid my reflections will probably only reveal how little I understand about the real problems psychotherapists are dealing with. If so, I can only apologise, and revert to the excuse that in my work I am intent on observing the evolution of the whole civilization. When all's said and done, though, Sorokin's message is: it is people, and their choices, that determine what happens.

I read a book which included the phrase "between the stimulus and the response comes the space", and went on to explain that it didn't matter whether the stimulus was genetic or environmental, we have the capacity to determine our response. This is contrary to most modern assumptions. Day after day scientists, especially biologists (physicists are more circumspect) on radio, TV and in the Press express their conviction that everything is materially determined.

I have just been reading David C Korten's *When Corporations Rule the World*, and rather unexpectedly towards the end, he distinguishes "Transcendental monism, which holds that matter arises from consciousness" with "Materialist monism, which sees consciousness as arising from matter." He sees in the former the only hope of a transformation of consciousness which will empower humanity to combat the destructive forces of materialism now rampant in the "global economy". It's much what Sorokin was saying when he declared that our vision of where Reality ultimately resides, whether wholly in, or beyond, the material world, determines whether a civilization prospers or declines.

"The rock on which modern medicine is foundering
is in no sese the efficacy of its procedures, but the view of life
on which it has based those procedures, often without
either discussion or reflection.
It is in philosophy that it is failing - or rather lacking."

Dethlesfsen & Dahlke

Biographical notes

Doris Lessing was born in 1919 and spent her childhood on a large farm in Southern Rhodesia. When she first came to England in 1949 she brought her first novel, *The Grass is Singing*, which was published in 1950 with outstanding international success. Since then her international reputation, not only as a novelist, but as a nonfiction and short-story writer, has flourished.

Michael Yapko is a clinical psychologist and director of the Milton Erickson Institute of San Diego. His many books include, *Trancework: An introduction to the practice of clinical hypnosis, When Living Hurts, Hypnosis and the Treatment of Depressions. Suggestions of Abuse, Essentials of Hypnosis.*

Andrew Weil M.D. graduated from Harvard Medical School. He has worked for the U.S. National Institute of Mental Health and for 15 years as a research associate in Ethnopharmacology at the Havard Botanical Museum. He has travelled widely, researching the medicinal properties of plants, altered states of consciousness and healing. He is currently Associate Director of the Division of Social Perspectives in Medicine and Director of the Programme of Integrative Medicine at the University of Arizona in Tuscon, USA. He practises natural and preventive medicine calling on a wide range of alternative therapies.

Jack Gibson, FRCSI, DTM & H (Lond.) graduated from the Royal College of Surgeons Dublin in 1933, having won almost every available medal. He gained his fellowship in 1934, the youngest ever to be awarded this distinction. He then obtained the Diploma of Tropical Medicine and Hygiene from London in 1935. He took two locums, one in Aden and the second in Malawi. After a hospital appointment in England he returned to Africa as Dean of the Native Medical Aids School, forerunner of the present Durban Medical School.

After the outbreak of war, he worked in England as a surgeon in the hospitals of the Emergency Medical Service. He later returned to Ireland as County Surgeon in Naas, Co. Kildare.

He has performed over 4,000 operations using hypnosis alone. Since retiring from surgery in 1979 he has devoted his time to the treatment of psychosomatic disorders using hypnotherapy.

Richard Webster studied English Literature at the University of East Anglia where he also taught. His first book, *A Brief History of Blasphemy: Liberalism, Censorship and The Satanic Verses* was published in 1990.

Robin Skynner was born in Charlestown on the south Cornish coast to a family of sea-farers. He saw active service in the RAF during the second world war. After the war he qualified in medicine at University College Hospital, London and began his lifelong interest in psychotherapeutic techniques pioneering group and family treatment and becoming one of the founders of both the Institute of Group Analysis and the Institute of Family Therapy (London). He has applied the ideas learned there to a range of group situations including companies, schools, hospitals, the social services and the clergy.

As well as being co-author with John Cleese of *Families and How To Survive Them* and *Life and How to Survive It,* he is author of *One Flesh: Separate Persons; Principles of Family* and *Marital Psychotherapy, Explorations* with *Families: Group Analysis* and *Family Therapy and Institutes and How To Survive Them: Mental Health Training and Consultation.*

James Roose-Evans is an innovative director of such pieces as his own adaptation of Helen Hanff's *84 Charing Cross Road* and Hugh Whitmore's *The Best of Friends* with Sir John Gielgud. He is the founder of the Hampstead Theatre in London and founder and director of the Bleddfa Trust in Wales. In 1981 he was the first British theatre director to be ordained a non-stipendiary priest. His books include a number on the theatre and several for children including the *Odd and Elsewhere* series.

He was on the Faculties of the Julliard School of Music, New York and the Royal Society of Dramatic Art in London. He was also Gian-Carlo Menotti Artist-in-Residence at Charleston, and the Distinguished Visiting Fellow at Ohio State University.

Anne Glyn-Jones read PPE at Oxford and then worked in Geneva for the World Health Organisation and Ottawa for the National Film Board of Canada. She also spent 5 years acting and stage managing in repertory and television. She was research archivist to Prime Minister Harold Macmillan in the preparation of his memoirs and then was, for 12 years Devon Research Fellow at the University of Exeter where she published a number of reports and articles on aspects of public policy. Her book, *Holding up* a Mirror - *How Civilizations Decline,* is published by Century.